"So, What do you eat?"

copyright : Liz Cook 1999
published by Liz Cook 1999

☎ 01273 388864

Distribution:

ISBN №: 0 9536222 07

To order books, or the full-size (88 x 18cm) laminated vesion of the nutrient wall - chart on the back page, please contact:

Liz Cook   OR: Stewart Distribution

☎ 01273   ☎ 01273 625988
      388864   E:MAIL STEWARTDIST@USA.NET
                          www.stewartdistribution.com

Printed on Chlorine-free paper

Liz Cook

Liz Cook has a degree (BSc. Hons) in Catering Management with Nutrition. 20 years a vegetarian, 8 years a vegan, she is a Schools Speaker for Viva! and Animal Aid, and has a robustly healthy 8-year old son, brought up vegan since birth. Liz produced the ubiquitous nutrient wall-chart! (see mini-version at back of book).

☺ Thanks to my brother Tim, my Mum and my Dad ☺

♥ For my son, Jamie Bickes Cook ♥

Contents

	Page
First Bit	1-2
Guide to Nutrition	
PROTEIN	3
Essential Fatty Acids	3
Vitamin A & B Group	4
Vitamin B₁₂ & C	5
Vitamin D, E, & K	6
IRON & CALCIUM	7
ZINC & IODINE	8
MAGNESIUM & OTHERS	9
Carbohydrates & Fibre	10
BREAKFAST	11
MAIN MEAL SOUPS	
Minestrone	13
Winter Vegetable Soup	14
Chinese Soup	15
Spicy Lentil Soup	16
Barley Soup	17
PASTA	
Almost Instant Noodles	18
Spaghetti Bolognese	19
Pasta & Pesto	20
Macaroni "Cheese"	21
Pasta & Green Beans	22
RICE & THINGS	
Mild Coconut Curry	23
Risotto	24
Chilli non Carne	25
Stir-Fry & Rice	26
Miso Vegetables & Tofu	27
Fried Tofu / Sweet and Sour Sauce	28
BEANS & LENTILS	
Mediterranean Beans	29
Butterbean Casserole	30
Barbecue Beans	31
Green Lentil & Spinach Hotpot	32
Aduki Bean & Sweet Potato Hotpot	33
PIES, PASTIES & POTATOES	
Chickpea Rissoles	34
Shepherdess Pie	35
Vegetable Pasties	36
Vegetable Crumble	37

	Page
SAVOURY PANCAKES	38
PIZZAS	39
ROAST DINNERS	
Lentil Roast	40
Cashew Loaf	41
Apple Sauce / Spicy Tomato	42
Sauce / Gravy	42
VEGETABLES	
Ratatouille	43
Roast Potatoes	44
Roasted Root Vegetables	44
Home-made chips / Jacket	45
potatoes / Steamed Vegetables	45
SALADS	46
Pink Potato Salad / Pasta Salad	47
Rice Salad / Coleslaw	48
Chickpeas & Garlic	49
Green Leafy Salad & Toasted seeds	49
Beansprouts / Sundried Tomatoes	50
Vinaigrette / Toasted seeds	51
TEA-TIME IDEAS	
Stuffed Pitta Bread / Sandwiches	52
Hummous Dip / Rice & Oat Cakes	53
Beans on Toast / Hot Dogs	54
Veggie Burgers	54
CAKES & PUDDINGS	
Vanilla Sponge	55
Chocolate Cake	56
"Cut & Come Again" Loaf	57
Apple Pie	58
Fruit Crumble	59
Upside-down-Pudding	60
Fruit Salad / Mango Hedgehog	61
Rice Pudding / Custard	62
Fruit Scones	63
Flapjacks	64
Home-made jelly	65
Baked Bananas / Banana Cream	65
Sweet Ideas	66
Conversion Charts	67
Shopping List!	68

FIRST BIT...

"I've got a lettuce in", said my Grandma when I went to stay with her. "No animal products? So what do you eat?" "What about your iron?" "...your son's protein?" "But it must take hours to cook..."

Well, it is perfectly possible to eat wonderful food, much of it easy and simple to cook, and to have an amazingly healthy, well-balanced & compassionate diet, without using animal products. Read on...

A Bit about Nutrition:

Pages 3-10 explain about each nutrient in detail and on the back of the book is an at-a-glance chart to help you balance your diet properly. Try and see if you can have something from each box every day. When cooking, it is a good idea to make the biggest part of your meal the carbohydrate eg: the rice, other wholegrains (bread, pastry, oats, millet), pasta or potato. The second biggest part should be the vegetables (including something green and leafy!). Then there should be a smaller quantity of high protein food like tofu, beans, nuts & seeds or even veggie sausages. And lastly a little "good" fat eg: olive or sesame oil, avocado or nuts & seeds. Eat a good mixture of all the foods in this book and the occasional "veggie-burger, chips & coke" day will not be too terrible!

A Bit about Ingredients:

Some foods in the book may be new to you: eg: <u>Tofu</u> - a soya bean curd, used for frying or in soups.
<u>Tahini</u>: sesame seed paste. <u>Miso</u>: fermented soya bean paste - like stock. <u>Bouillon</u>: a vegetable stock powder.
<u>Tamari</u>: pure soya sauce (much nicer than soy sauce!).
<u>Nori</u>: crisp sheets of sea-weed. <u>Soya Milk</u>: look out for sweetened, calcium-fortified ones like "Plamil" (with B_{12} added too) and Provamel. <u>Rice syrup</u>: clear sweet syrup - use like honey.

What about organic food?

Yes! More and more people are thinking that we don't need a diet of fertilizers, pesticides and additives! And nobody is sure how safe genetically engineered foods (G.M.O's) are going to be. With organic vegetables you don't need to peel them to get rid of harmful chemicals and so you keep all the valuable vitamins and minerals just under the skin. Organic food _is_ more expensive but will get cheaper the more it is bought!

Some things to avoid:

Try, if possible, to avoid too much salt and too much sugar. Also, try and avoid too much processed food; food with hydrogenated, or trans-fatty, acids (look on the labels). Also avoid food with loads of additives, preservatives, flavourings and colourings. Don't eat too much fried food..!

A Bit about oils:

Good oil is very important. Buy the best you can afford – preferably organic, cold-pressed extra virgin in a dark bottle!! Cheap, poor-quality over-processed oil is not good for you. Keep oil in the dark and cold – the fridge is best. Never re-use heated oil. For margarines, again buy organic, non-hydrogenated ones, free from trans-fatty acids. (Some will be B_{12} fortified – this is useful.)

About the Recipes:

The recipes assume you have some basic cooking skills and should be fairly simple. They are usually for about **6 people** but this depends totally on how big and hungry those people are! They are generous recipes so that you can keep some in the fridge for the next day. Some recipes take more time so I've suggested freezing some for another day.

Measurements: these are in metric (for the new millenium!) but there is an Imperial conversion chart (p 67).

Equipment: Useful things : a good set of sharp knives, a steamer, a wok, stainless-steel or cast-iron pans, a hand-blender and someone else to wash-up.

Guide to Nutrition

PROTEIN

What for: Protein is the building blocks of the body - used for making & repairing cells, hormones & antibodies.

How much: The recommended amounts are:

Age: 1-3 years - 14.5g/day   4-6 ys. - 19.5g/day

7-10 ys. - 28.3g/day   11-14 ys. - 42g/day

Adult 45-50g/day   (1oz = 28g)

Not enough: This is highly unlikely. Protein needs are automatically met by a varied, balanced diet.

Found in: Lots of foods - beans, pulses, nuts, seeds, tofu cereals, rice, wholegrains, bread, soya milk - even potatoes.

Essential Fatty Acids *

What for: Fatty acids make up fats. Two EFA's * we must get from our food are linoleic & linolenic acids. Fats provide energy, protect the organs, help the body use the fat-soluble vitamins A, D, E & K & help hormone action.

How much: This is still not yet decided, but in a good diet there will be plenty. The important thing is to eat good quality, cold-pressed virgin oils - organic if possible - and try and cut down on processed & fried foods.

Not enough: Unlikely. Extra EFA's do seem to benefit some skin problems and P.M.T.

Found in: Vegetable oils (see chart on back), green vegetables & grains, seeds, nuts.

Vitamin A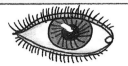

What for: Vitamin A is a fat-soluble vitamin used to help us see in the dark. It is also used for normal growth of body tissues and to keep our skin and gums healthy. It also helps fight infection and is anti-oxidant.

How much: There will be plenty in a healthy diet. (In very large doses, Vitamin A is toxic).

Not enough: Very unlikely as the body can store it in the liver. Where there is a problem there may be sore gums, skin problems and night blindness.

Found in: Carotene in carrots, yellow vegetables, mango, apricot, margarine and green vegetables.

Vitamin B Group

What For: The vitamin B group are water-soluble vitamins used for growth, energy and protein use; the functioning of the nervous system and the prevention of anaemia.

How much: Different amounts are recommended. However....

Not enough: Unlikely in a varied wholefood diet but good to pay attention to a good supply.

Found in: Wholegrains, yeast extract, green leafy veg. Because B vitamins are water soluble, it is best to steam vegetables or eat them raw. The B Vitamins are:

B_1 = Thiamin, B_2 = Riboflavin, B_3 = Niacin, B_6 = Pyridoxin, Folic acid (folate), Pantothenic Acid & Biotin & B_{12} ...read on....

Vitamin B₁₂

What for: Vitamin B₁₂ is a water-soluble vitamin used in the healthy working of the nervous system and to form blood in the bone marrow.

How much: The body needs tiny amounts of B₁₂ and can store it. B₁₂ is measured in micrograms (μg). The daily amount recommended for the average adult is $1.2-1.5 \mu g$.

Not enough: Despite concern over B₁₂, it is very rare to find signs of deficiency. This is not fully understood and research into B₁₂ is still going on, so find a B₁₂ food:

Found in: The most reliable foods in a non-animal diet are fortified products eg: Plamil soya milk, yeast extract, soya mince and animal-free margarines and cereals.

Vitamin C

What for: Vitamin C is another water-soluble vitamin used for forming body cells, fighting infection, healing wounds and helping the body absorb iron.

How much: The recommended amounts are 25-30 mg/day for children and 40 mg/day for adults.

Not enough: This is a possibility as Vitamin C is easily destroyed by heat, light and length of storage. Get vegetables and fruit as fresh as possible and steam them or eat them raw. Eat lots!

Found in: Oranges, mangoes, strawberries, blackcurrants, broccoli, frozen peas, green leafy vegetables and parsley. And potatoes!

Vitamin D

What for: Vitamin D is a fat-soluble vitamin used with calcium & phosphorus to make bones.
How much: There are no exact recommended amounts.
Not enough: This is unlikely unless you are never outside.
Where from: Sunlight (non necessarily sunshine) on the skin. Even bare hands and face are enough. Vitamin D_2 is also added to some cereals and margarine. (D_3 is an animal product).

Vitamin E

What for: Vitamin E is fat-soluble. It is used in the reproductive system; for healthy blood; to slow down aging and for a healthy immune system.
How much: There are no recommended amounts.
Not enough: Extremely unlikely in wholefood diets.
Found in: Dark green vegetables, soya beans wholegrains, vegetable oils, nuts & avocados.

Vitamin K

What for: Vitamin K's most important function is to help blood clotting and for healthy body tissues.
How much: There is not really a recommended amount.
Not enough: This almost never happens.
Found in: Green leafy vegetables, broccoli, cauliflower, fruit and grains.

MINERALS

IRON

What for: Iron is used for making blood, carrying oxygen, preventing anaemia and making enzymes.

How much: The recommended amounts are between 7.8mg and 14.8 mg/day.

Not enough: This can happen (surprisingly just as much in meat eaters). Signs of not enough can be: tiredness, breathlessness, headaches & poor concentration. The thing with iron is not only how much is <u>eaten</u> but how much is <u>absorbed</u>. To help absorption, avoid tea & coffee with meals, and eat Vitamin C rich foods. No problem!

Found in: Pulses, dried fruit, wholegrains, tofu, green leafy vegetables & blackstrap molasses....

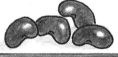

CALCIUM

What for: Calcium is the "building material" of bones and teeth. It is also used for the heart, nerves and muscles.

How much: The recommended amounts are between 350 and 550 mg/day for children; 800-1,000 mg/day for teenagers and 700 mg/day for adult

Not enough: Unlikely, but it is important that there is enough Vitamin D and not too much protein or saturated fats. No problem in balanced animal-free diet!

Found in: Tofu, nuts and seeds (try tahini), green leafy vegetables, broccoli, swede and fortified soya milks.

ZINC

What for: Zinc is needed for healing wounds, keeping the immune system strong (fighting colds for example...) and for the heart and reproductive organs.

How much: The recommended amounts are 4-7 mg for children, 9 mg for teenagers & 7-9.5mg for adults, (daily).

Not enough: This is unlikely but signs can be tiredness, loss of appetite, wounds may be slow to heal and, in extreme cases, sterility.

Found in: Soybeans, spinach, sunflower and pumpkin seeds, wheatgerm, wholegrains, oats, pulses, lentils, nuts, miso and mushrooms.

IODINE

What for: Iodine is needed for a healthy thyroid gland which controls our metabolism (the rate of body activity) It is also needed for energy & for hair, skin, nails & teeth.

How much: The recommended amounts are 70 mcg/day for 1-3 year olds, 100 mcg/day for 4-10 years; 140 mcg/day for average adults.

Not enough: This is a possibility. Signs of possible lack are: cold hands and feet, nervousness & obesity. It is a good idea to pay attention to iodine sources and include some regularly (NB: too much is toxic).

Found in: Edible seaweeds, (such as kelp, dulse, wakami, hijiki & nori). (Try toasted sushi nori – to nibble or make sushi – it's yummy) Also sea-salt & fortified foods.

MAGNESIUM

What for: Magnesium is used in making bones, muscles, nerves and teeth. Also for heart, arteries and use of energy.

How much: The recommended amounts are: 85-200 mg for children, 270-300 mg. for adults.

Not enough: Very unlikely. There will be enough in a good diet.

Found in: Wholegrains, green leafy vegetables, nuts and soya beans. Yeast extract, sea-weed and millet.

Phosphorous, Sulphur, Potassium

What for: These are used in the healthy working of nerves, skin, bones, teeth, muscles, organs and energy use.

How much: Amounts vary, but there will be plenty in your diet and deficiencies are almost unknown.

Found in: Dried fruit, bananas, potatoes, nuts and pulses, yeast extract, wholegrains and wheat —germ.

Others: Fluorine/Copper/Cobalt/Chromium/Silicon Selenium/Manganese/Vanadium/Sodium Chloride/Molybdenum.

What for: Many different parts of the body need these trace elements. Enzymes, teeth and bones, energy use, growth and fluid balance all need these. There will be plenty in your diet.

Found in: Wholegrains, beans and pulses, nuts, vegetables, fruit and brewer's yeast.

Carbohydrates

What for: Carbohydrates provide us with energy, body fat and fibre.

How much: This depends on : how big you are, how old you are, how much energy you use and other factors. It is very unlikely you will not have enough **but** it is important to eat <u>complex</u> carbohydrates - not lots of sugar and white flour (simple carbohydrates).

Where from: Good healthy sources of carbohydrates are : wholegrains, rice, wholemeal bread, cereals, oats, beans and pulses, pasta and potatoes.

FIBRE

ON AN ANIMAL-FREE DIET — NO PROBLEM ! ☺

What for: Fibre is a vital part of our diet - it does not digest, and provides bulk to help the healthy working of our intestines as they get rid of waste.

How much: The recommended amount is 20-40g/day. In general people should eat more fibre-rich food than they do in the modern diet.

Not enough: This is quite likely and can cause constipation, irritable bowel syndrome and has links with obesity, heart-disease and colon cancer.

Found in: Wholegrains, nuts, beans & pulses, oats and fruit and vegetables.

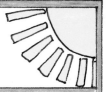

Surprisingly, non-animal food breakfast can be much the same as traditional breakfast!

Using soya-milk and animal-free margarine r cereals, breakfast is very simple.

Cereals

If you like them, any number of pre-packeted cereals are animal-free (Vitamin D_2 is non-animal, vitamin D_3 is animal-derived if you see them on a packet) Try some of the organic, sugar-free ones.

Muesli

You can buy it ready-made or buy a base-mix from health-food shops and add some or all of these: fruit r nuts, sesame, sunflower r pumpkin seeds, bananas raisins, sultanas, chopped dried dates or apricots.

Porridge (for two)

1 cup of porridge oats
2 cups of soya milk or 1 cup milk/1 cup water.

o Put all the ingredients in a pan and bring to the boil, STIRRING CONSTANTLY.

o Serve with a bit of syrup and soya milk. Mmm....

Pancakes – see page 38.

Toast...

Try and use wholemeal bread if you can (organic is even better). Try these ideas :
- Tahini + pear-and-apple spread + banana ...
- Peanut or cashew nut butter r marmalade.
- Yeast extract (low-salt is good) or marmite with cucumber or tomato.

Also try and use good quality, non-hydrogenated animal-free margarine — wholefood shops have lots!

'Fry-ups'

A big pile of fried food every day isn't the best idea but now and again is fine. Try frying any (or all !) of these in olive oil :

- Left-over cooked potatoes
- Fresh tomatoes
- Mushrooms
- "Rashers" (soya bacon)
- Veggie sausages

Add : Baked beans, tinned tomatoes ...
One of my favourites is fried tomatoes, mushrooms, garlic r chopped herbs (coriander or parsley), with a bit of tamari and lots of freshly ground black pepper.

Fruit Salad

Not just good for pudding — mixed fresh fruit is great breakfast food — grapefruits, apples, bananas, kiwis, grapes, oranges ... add to cereal... or yoghurt.

Minestrone Soup

200g potatoes
250g broccoli
250g carrots
1 large onion
3 cloves garlic
200g frozen peas
1 tin chopped tomatoes
Small bunch fresh oregano
2 sheets toasted nori
1 veg. stock cube or 1 tbs bouillon
125g spaghetti
2 tbs miso
Olive oil
S & p.

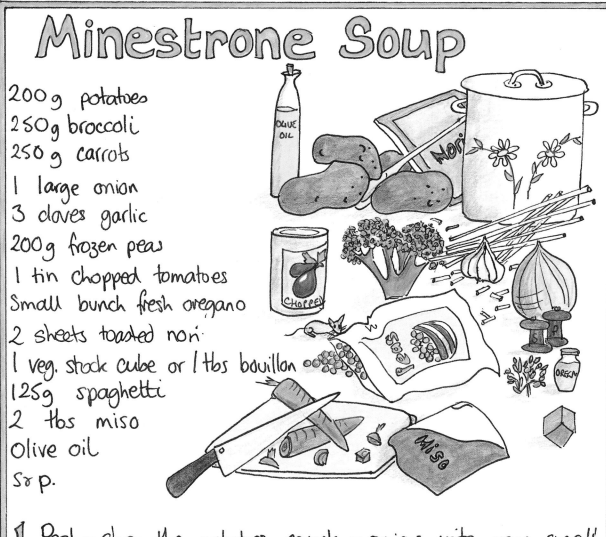

1. Peel & chop the potatoes, carrots & onions into very small cubes (about 1cm) and chop the garlic.
2. Fry the vegetables gently in enough olive oil to cover the bottom of a large pan. Stir occasionally. Add oregano.
3. Meanwhile: make the stock: dissolve the stock cube or bouillon in 2 pints boiling water. Add nori in small pieces. Add the stock & tomatoes to the pan.
4. Bring to the boil. Break the spaghetti into 1" (2cm) lengths and add to the pan.
5. When spaghetti is soft add the broccoli (chopped into small pieces). Add frozen peas. Cook for 2 minutes.
6. Turn off heat & add miso. Stir in well.
7. Season with salt & pepper & eat with crusty bread.

Winter Vegetable Soup

500g potatoes
300g carrots
2 large onions
4 cloves garlic
1 large leek
300g parsnips
300g swede
small bunch chopped parsley
2 vegetable stock cubes or
      2 tbs. bouillon.
Olive oil
Salt r pepper.

This makes lots - so freeze half.

YOU WILL NEED A BLENDER

1. Peel and chop the potatoes, parsnips, swede and carrots roughly into 2cm cubes. Wash and slice the leeks and peel and chop the onions and garlic

2. Put enough olive oil in a big pan to cover the bottom and gently fry the vegetables in this order: potatoes, swede, parsnips, carrots, leeks, onions and garlic. With the lid on, cook gently, stirring occasionally until the vegetables are really soft.

3. Meanwhile: make the stock: add the stock cube or bouillon to 2 pints of boiling water. Add to the pan and bring to the boil. Simmer for 5-10 minutes.

4. Blend in the pan with a hand-blender or in a food processor.

5. Add salt r pepper to taste and serve with the finely chopped parsley. Eat with crusty bread. Lovely!

Chinese Soup

250g leeks
250g carrots
250g cabbage
2 sheets nori (seaweed)
100g beansprouts
200g tofu
½ a green & ½ a red pepper.
small tin sweetcorn
1" cube ginger (fresh)
3 cloves garlic
Small bunch fresh coriander
50g rice noodles
4 tbs miso
1 tbs cumin (powder)
Tamari

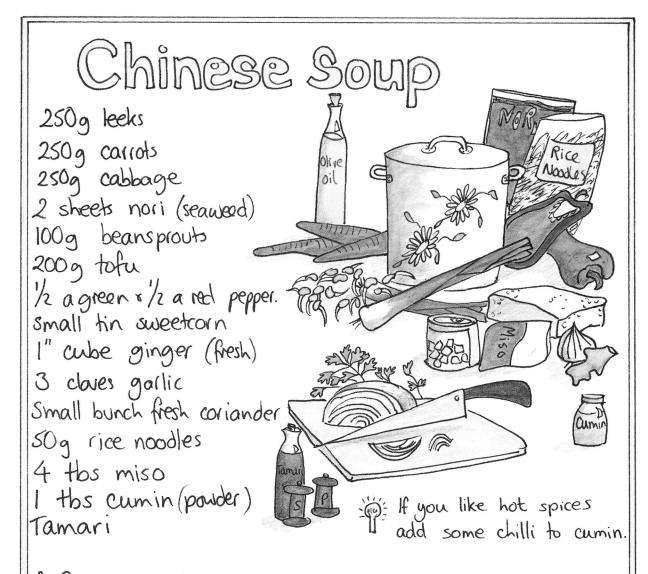

If you like hot spices add some chilli to cumin.

1. Peel & chop the carrots into little sticks. Chop the peppers into slices. Finely slice the cabbage & leeks. Peel & finely chop the garlic & ginger.
2. Gently fry the vegetables in enough olive oil to cover the bottom of a large pan. Add the cumin. Stir.
3. Meanwhile: make the stock. Add the broken up nori to 2½ pints of boiling water. Add to the vegetables.
4. Add the rice noodles, chopped coriander to the pan. Cut the tofu into ½" cubes (1 cm) & add. Add the beansprouts & sweetcorn.
5. Turn off the heat & add the miso. Stir in well & put the lid on until the rice noodles are soft.
6. Season with tamari & black pepper & serve with hot toast.

(15)

Spicy Lentil Soup

250g dried red lentils
250g onions
3 cloves garlic
250g carrots
250g leeks
small bunch parsley
3 bay leaves
1 tbs. cumin powder
4 tbs. tamari
Olive oil.
salt & pepper.

1. Peel and roughly chop the carrots, onions, leeks and garlic.

2. Fry the vegetables slowly in enough olive oil to cover the bottom of a large pan and stir occasionally. Add the cumin and cook until the vegetables are almost soft.

3. Add 2½ pints of boiling water, the bay leaves and lentils. Bring to the boil, turn down the heat and simmer for about 10 minutes until the lentils are soft.

4. Add tamari and salt and pepper to taste.

5. Remove the bay leaves and blend the soup.

6. Chop the parsley and garnish the soup. Serve with crusty french bread. Eat with a green leafy salad as a main meal. Yum...

This makes a lot and freezes well. Keep some for another day!

Barley Soup

250g pearl barley
250g onions
3 cloves garlic
250g carrots
200g spinach
1 leek
4 sticks celery
250g parsnip and/or swede
200g potatoes
small bunch parsley
olive oil
1 stock cube or 1 tbs bouillon powder

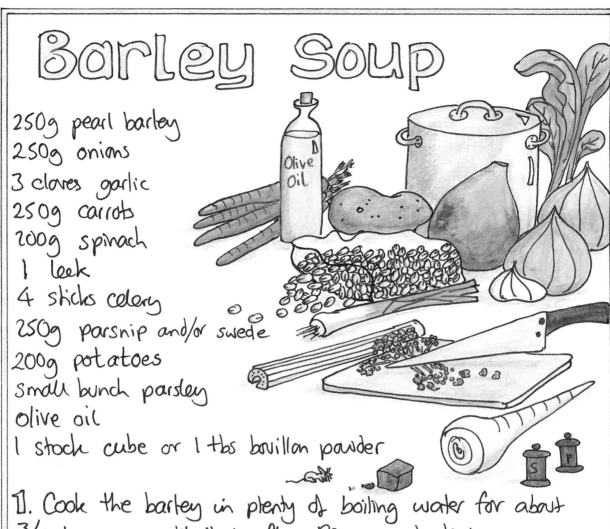

1. Cook the barley in plenty of boiling water for about 3/4 hour or until it is soft. Rinse and drain.
2. Meanwhile: peel and chop the onions, garlic, carrots, swede, parsnip, leek and potatoes into 1-2cm pieces and fry very slowly in enough olive oil to cover the bottom of a large pan
3. Meanwhile: make the stock: add the stock cube or bouillon powder to 2 pints of boiling water to the pan with the barley.
4. Chop the celery and spinach and add to the pan.
5. Add the fried vegetables, bring to the boil and simmer until all the vegetables are soft.
6. Season with salt and pepper. Add more boiling water if necessary.
7. Serve with chopped parsley and crusty wholemeal bread. Will warm you up!

FREEZES WELL. IS EVEN BETTER NEXT DAY. (Recipe makes loads)

Almost Instant Noodles

500g noodles
450 g carrots
bunch chopped parsley
1-2cm cube ginger
3 cloves garlic
tamari to taste
mixed seeds : ½ cup :
sunflower / pumpkin / sesame.
fresh or dried chilli

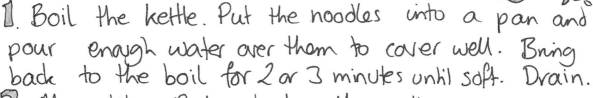

1. Boil the kettle. Put the noodles into a pan and pour enough water over them to cover well. Bring back to the boil for 2 or 3 minutes until soft. Drain.
2. Meanwhile : Peel and chop the garlic & ginger & fry very gently (almost just warming) in a frying pan. Add the tamari and mixed seeds.
3. Meanwhile grate the carrots and put aside.
4. If you use it, chop the chilli (only use a little to start with) and add. Or a pinch of chilli powder. (wash your hands straight away).
5. Stir in the noodles. Season with salt & pepper.
6 Add the grated carrots & chopped parsley.
7 Serve immediately. Eat loads !

Try: a squeeze of lime or lemon, chopped coriander instead of parsley & cashew nuts instead of seeds. **Try:** Spinach noodles...   Really quick, easy & yummy.

Spaghetti Bolognese

250g carrots
250g onions
3 cloves garlic
1 red pepper
125g mushrooms
1 small bunch parsley
1 tsp dried oregano & basil
1 vegetable stock cube or bouillon
1 tin chopped tomatoes
1 small tin tomato purée
250g red lentils
1 packet (500g) spaghetti
Olive oil.

* Black olives are good in this, if you like them!

1. Peel and chop the onions, garlic, carrots & fry them gently in enough olive oil to cover the bottom of a pan.
2. Wash & chop the pepper & mushrooms and add to the pan. Chop and add the parsley & herbs.
3. When the vegetables are nearly soft, add the lentils & 700ml (1¼ pints) of water. Bring to the boil and simmer until the lentils are soft, stirring regularly. Season.
4. Add the tomatoes, purée, vegetable stock or bouillon & olives if used.   Simmer gently.
5. Cook the spaghetti (follow instructions on packet)
6. Serve the spaghetti with the sauce on top. Eat with crusty french bread and green salad. Grated soya cheese is good on top too.

Make double & freeze some...

Pasta and Pesto

(VERY QUICK & EASY)

500g any pasta (bows are good)
dash of tamari
2 tbs. vegan pesto
2 tbs. olive oil
Add some (or all!) of:
1 tbs. pine kernels
1 tbs. cashew nuts
bunch parsley, chopped.
½ cup black olives
25 g. fried mushrooms
½ avocado.

1. Cook the pasta in plenty of boiling water.
2. Meanwhile: gently heat the oil and stir in all the extra ingredients, and the pesto & tamari.
3. Add the pesto mixture and stir in to the pasta. Eat with green salad & french bread.

Home-made Pesto

(EASY!)*

3 tbs. olive oil
2 tbs. pumpkin seeds
2 tbs. sunflower seeds
2 tbs. sesame seeds
2 tbs. pine kernels
2 tbs. lemon juice
2 tbs. creamed basil (jar)
   (or big bunch chopped fresh)

1. Blend all the ingredients. Add lots of fresh black pepper & salt to taste. Store in a jar in the fridge.

*(YOU WILL NEED A BLENDER)

Macaroni 'Cheese'

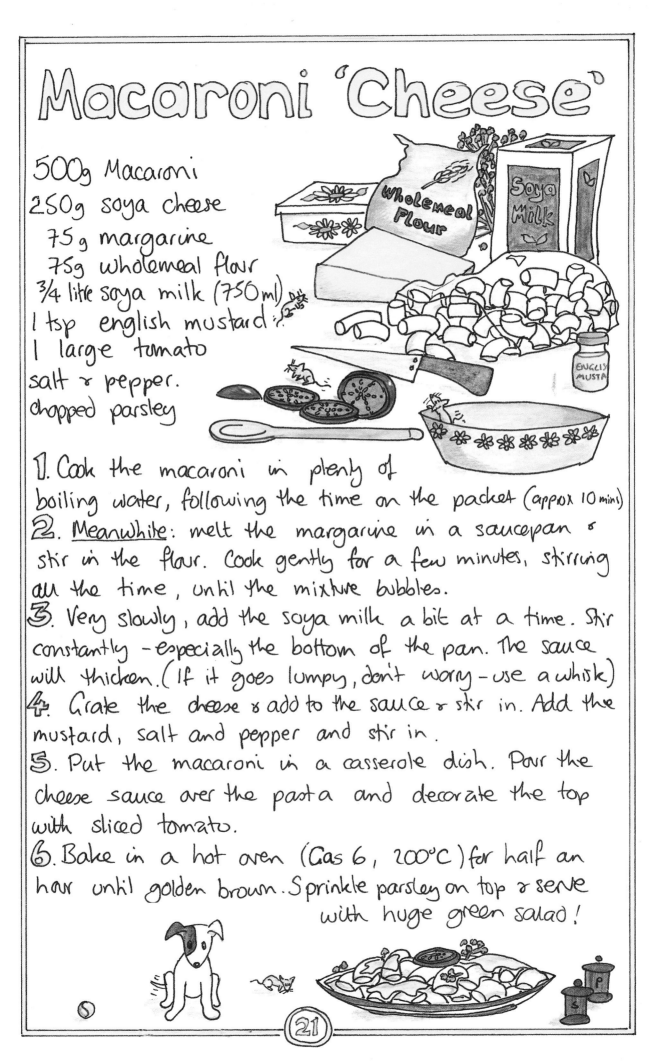

500g Macaroni
250g soya cheese
75g margarine
75g wholemeal flour
3/4 litre soya milk (750ml)
1 tsp english mustard
1 large tomato
salt & pepper.
chopped parsley

1. Cook the macaroni in plenty of boiling water, following the time on the packet (approx 10 mins)

2. Meanwhile: melt the margarine in a saucepan & stir in the flour. Cook gently for a few minutes, stirring all the time, until the mixture bubbles.

3. Very slowly, add the soya milk a bit at a time. Stir constantly - especially the bottom of the pan. The sauce will thicken. (If it goes lumpy, don't worry - use a whisk)

4. Grate the cheese & add to the sauce & stir in. Add the mustard, salt and pepper and stir in.

5. Put the macaroni in a casserole dish. Pour the cheese sauce over the pasta and decorate the top with sliced tomato.

6. Bake in a hot oven (Gas 6, 200°C) for half an hour until golden brown. Sprinkle parsley on top & serve with huge green salad!

Pasta & Green Beans
(V. Quick one)

500g any sort of pasta
  (tagliatelle is good)
3 cloves garlic
1 large onion
500g french beans (or
    other green beans)
1 tin chopped tomatoes
small bunch fresh herbs:
    basil / coriander / parsley
salt & pepper

YOU CAN ADD SOME OLIVES OR FRIED MUSHROOMS

1. Wash, 'end' and chop the green beans into 1cm pieces. Peel and chop the onion and garlic.
2. Fry the vegetables very gently in enough olive oil to cover the bottom of a pan. Let beans soften.
3. Cook the pasta in plenty of boiling water (see instructions on the packet).
4. Finely chop the herbs & add the tin of chopped tomatoes and the herbs to the beans. Simmer gently for a few minutes.
5. Season with salt & black pepper. Serve with crusty french bread, & soya cheese (grated) if you like it. So easy & delicious!

Mild Coconut Curry

2 tsp. mild curry paste (or powder).
1 tin coconut milk
1 tin chick peas (425g)
200 g potatoes
250 g onions
4 cloves garlic
250g broccoli
250g carrots
200g mushrooms
200g peppers (green or red)
small bunch fresh coriander
olive oil.

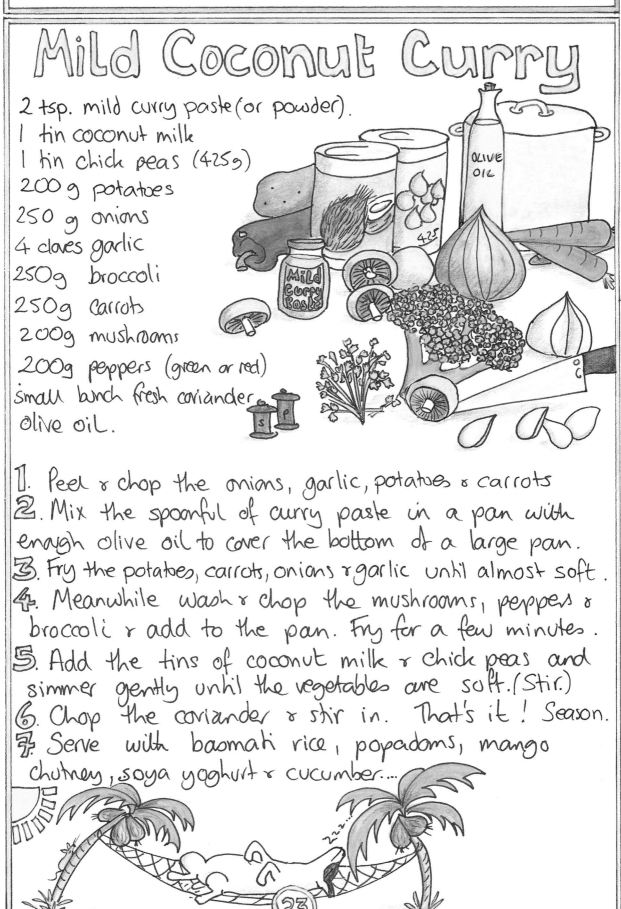

1. Peel & chop the onions, garlic, potatoes & carrots
2. Mix the spoonful of curry paste in a pan with enough olive oil to cover the bottom of a large pan.
3. Fry the potatoes, carrots, onions & garlic until almost soft.
4. Meanwhile wash & chop the mushrooms, peppers & broccoli & add to the pan. Fry for a few minutes.
5. Add the tins of coconut milk & chick peas and simmer gently until the vegetables are soft. (Stir.)
6. Chop the coriander & stir in. That's it! Season.
7. Serve with basmati rice, popadoms, mango chutney, soya yoghurt & cucumber....

Risotto

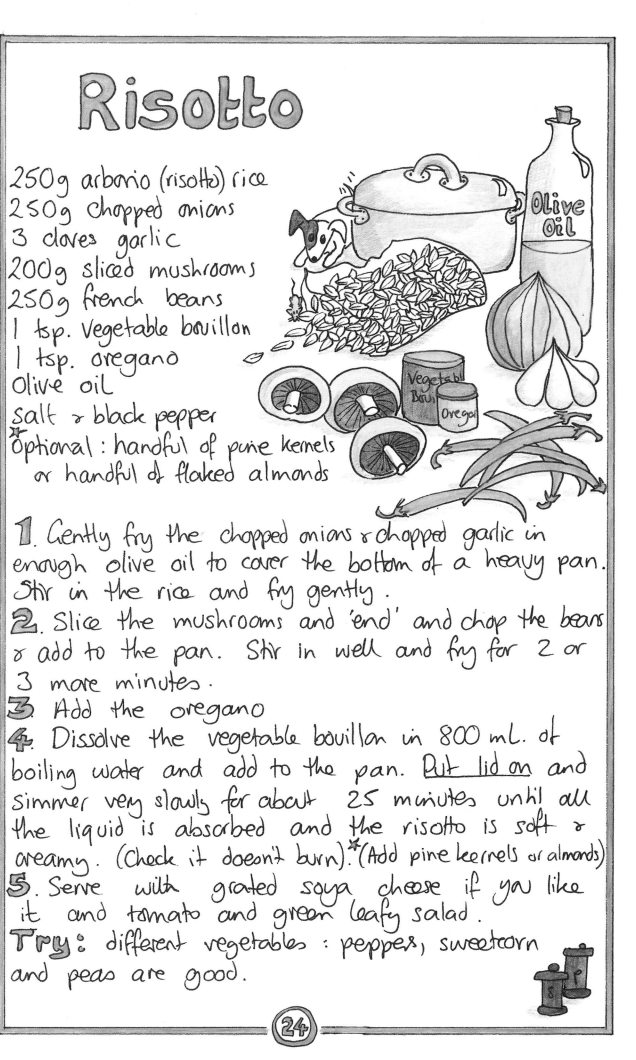

250g arborio (risotto) rice
250g chopped onions
3 cloves garlic
200g sliced mushrooms
250g french beans
1 tsp. Vegetable bouillon
1 tsp. oregano
Olive oil
Salt & black pepper
*Optional : handful of pine kernels
    or handful of flaked almonds

1. Gently fry the chopped onions & chopped garlic in enough olive oil to cover the bottom of a heavy pan. Stir in the rice and fry gently.
2. Slice the mushrooms and 'end' and chop the beans & add to the pan. Stir in well and fry for 2 or 3 more minutes.
3. Add the oregano
4. Dissolve the vegetable bouillon in 800 mL. of boiling water and add to the pan. Put lid on and simmer very slowly for about 25 minutes until all the liquid is absorbed and the risotto is soft & creamy. (Check it doesn't burn).*(Add pine kernels or almonds)
5. Serve with grated soya cheese if you like it and tomato and green leafy salad.
Try: different vegetables : peppers, sweetcorn and peas are good.

Chilli non Carne (quick one)

2 tins red kidney beans
250g carrots
300g potatoes
450g onions
 6 garlic cloves
300g red & yellow peppers
250g courgettes
200g mushrooms
Bottle olive oil
1 tsp. chilli powder or 1 fresh chilli*
small bunch fresh coriander
1 tin chopped tomatoes
1 small tin tomato purée (100g)
Salt & pepper

1. Peel & chop the carrots, potatoes and onions into small pieces. Chop the garlic. Fry together in olive oil in a large saucepan. Add the chilli and stir in. (chopped, if fresh)
2. Wash and chop the peppers, courgettes & mushrooms and add to the pan.
3. When the potatoes are soft, add tinned tomatoes, purée, kidney beans and chopped coriander. Season with lots of fresh ground pepper & salt.
4. Simmer for about 30 minutes on a low heat with a lid on, stirring occasionally.
5. Serve with rice, millet, corn chips, tortillas or tacos. Also good with jacket potatoes. (In which case cook the chilli in the oven for 30 minutes instead of on top). Eat with a big green salad. Spicy!

(* Chillis vary a lot in strength - try a little & add more if needed)

Stir-Fry & Rice

Stir-fries are great because you can choose from a wide range of different vegetables.* A basic recipe is:

Olive or sesame oil

250g carrots

250g onions

200g broccoli

200g courgettes

100g mushrooms

100g beansprouts

250g tofu

2 tbsp. tamari

3 cloves garlic

2½ cm ginger

1 tbsp. cumin powder

Bunch fresh coriander

1. Wash, peel and chop or slice all the vegetables into pieces (the carrots & courgettes are good in stick shapes).

2. Heat the oil gently in a wok if you have one or a large frying pan. Add the onions, garlic, ginger, cumin powder & tamari & fry quickly. Add the tofu. Fry.

3. Add the carrots, broccoli, mushrooms & courgettes. Lastly add the beansprouts & chopped coriander & fry quickly for another 5 minutes – stirring all the time.

4. Serve with rice or rice noodles. If you want make sweet and sour sauce (p.28). Also: toasted sushi nori is good to eat with this. If you like hot spices try serving with tabasco sauce or sprinkled dried chillis.

*Try: aubergines, cauliflower, spring onions, red & green peppers, chopped spinach, mange-touts, baby sweetcorn, cashew nuts, toasted seeds. Yum-Yum!

Miso Vegetables & Tofu

(A quick very-good-for-you one)

200g Wholegrain rice
200g tofu
350g (organic) broccoli
6 cloves garlic
1-2 cm cube ginger
Olive oil
1 tablespoon miso
Small bunch parsley
½ lemon

Try: 100g carrots & 100g cashew nuts instead of tofu.

1. Cook the rice: wash it and put in a heavy pan. Add water up to 2cm above the rice (1"). Bring to the boil, replace the lid and turn down heat. Simmer until the water is absorbed. (Add more water if needed but don't let rice go mushy).

2. Meanwhile: cut the tofu into 1" (2½ cm) cubes, chop up the broccoli, garlic & ginger. (Carrots too if used).

3. Heat some olive oil gently and add the vegetables. Cook gently for a few minutes. Add tofu (or cashew nuts)

4. When beginning to sizzle, add ½ pint (¼ litre) of water. Reduce the heat & put the lid on the pan.

5. When the vegetables are still crunchy, turn off the heat & add the miso. Stir in well.

6. Finely chop the parsley and add to the pan.

7. Serve with the rice, squeeze lemon juice over it.
Power Food!

Fried Tofu

250 g tofu
3 cloves garlic
2 cm cube ginger
1 tablespoon cumin powder
3 tablespoons tamari
Olive oil
Bunch fresh coriander

1. Peel and chop the garlic and ginger into small pieces. Cut the tofu into 2 cm cubes.
2. Mix the tofu, garlic, ginger, tamari and cumin together. Chop the coriander and mix in.
3. Fry the tofu gently in enough olive oil to cover the bottom of a pan. Serve with steamed veg. & rice.

Sweet & Sour Sauce

1 tin chopped tomatoes
1 dsp. tomato purée
1 clove garlic
1 tbsp. cider vinegar
1½ tbsp tamari
1 dsp. blackstrap molasses
70 ml. orange juice
1 tbsp. rice syrup
2 tsp. cornflour

1. Chop & peel the garlic. Put all the ingredients into a pan and blend. Season with black pepper.
2. Use a little of the liquid & mix cornflour to a paste.
3. Stir in to pan & bring to the boil, stirring non-stop!

BEANS & LENTILS

Mediterranean Beans

(Easy)

Olive oil
2 tins flageolet beans
or 300 g dried ones
2 sticks celery
1 large onion
3 cloves garlic
1 tin chopped tomatoes
1 tbsp. sundried tomato paste
small bunch fresh oregano
small bunch fresh parsley
3 bay leaves
salt and pepper

* You can do this with black-eyed beans, chick-peas or haricot beans too.

1. If using dried beans, soak them overnight, rinse and drain and cook in plenty of boiling water until soft. (approx 1 hour)
2. Peel and chop the onions and garlic. Chop the celery. Fry gently in enough oil to cover the bottom of a heavy pan, until the onions are soft.
3. Add the tinned tomatoes, sundried tomato paste, bay leaves and chopped oregano. Drain the beans & add.
4. Simmer gently for 20 minutes, stirring occasionally. Add lots of ground black pepper.
5. Serve with chopped parsley sprinkled on top and lots of crusty french bread. Mmm....

Butterbean Casserole

500g dried butterbeans
500g carrots
500g onions
6 cloves garlic
250g mushrooms
Small bunch parsley
50g wholemeal flour
1 litre sweetened soya milk
Olive oil
3 bay leaves
1 tbs. vegetable bouillon
4 tbs. tamari

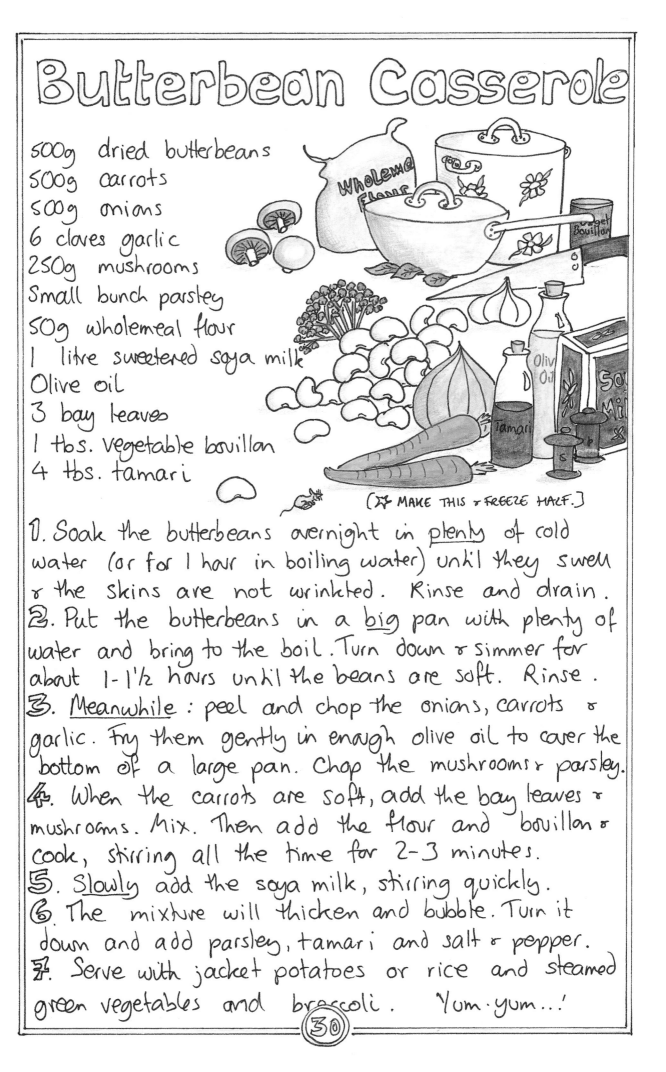

(☆ MAKE THIS & FREEZE HALF.)

1. Soak the butterbeans overnight in plenty of cold water (or for 1 hour in boiling water) until they swell & the skins are not wrinkled. Rinse and drain.

2. Put the butterbeans in a big pan with plenty of water and bring to the boil. Turn down & simmer for about 1-1½ hours until the beans are soft. Rinse.

3. Meanwhile : peel and chop the onions, carrots & garlic. Fry them gently in enough olive oil to cover the bottom of a large pan. Chop the mushrooms & parsley.

4. When the carrots are soft, add the bay leaves & mushrooms. Mix. Then add the flour and bouillon & cook, stirring all the time for 2-3 minutes.

5. Slowly add the soya milk, stirring quickly.

6. The mixture will thicken and bubble. Turn it down and add parsley, tamari and salt & pepper.

7. Serve with jacket potatoes or rice and steamed green vegetables and broccoli.   'Yum·yum...!'

Barbecue Beans
(with fried potatoes)

250g dried haricot beans
250g onions
250g potatoes
3 cloves garlic
100g tomato purée
1 tin chopped tomatoes
1 tsp. english mustard
1 dsp. blackstrap molasses
1 tbsp. rice syrup
2 tbsp. tamari
fresh ground black pepper
Olive oil

1. Soak the beans overnight. Next day, drain & rinse. Bring to the boil & simmer for 1-1½ hours until the beans are soft.

2. Meanwhile: clean & chop the potatoes into small cubes (1½cm) Peel & chop the onions & garlic. Fry the potatoes, onions and garlic in enough olive oil to cover the bottom of a large pan.

3. With a hand blender, blend all the rest of the ingredients. (If you don't have a blender, simply mix them).

4. When the potatoes are cooked and a bit browned, tip the beans & sauce into the large pan.

5. Season with black pepper & salt to taste. Simmer for 30 minutes, stirring occasionally.

6. Serve with crusty bread and salad.

THERE IS QUITE A LOT OF PREPARATION IN THIS, SO WHY NOT COOK DOUBLE & FREEZE HALF. IT FREEZES WELL. IT IS ALSO EVEN BETTER THE NEXT DAY.

Green Lentil & Spinach Hotpot

(REALLY TASTY - MUCH NICER THAN IT SOUNDS!)

300g green/brown lentils (dried)
350g fresh spinach
500g potatoes
200g carrots
250g leeks
250g onions
4 cloves garlic
2½ cm square ginger root
1 tbsp. cumin powder
2 tbsp. miso
vegetable stock cube or bouillon (1 tbs)
Olive oil.

- 😊 : MAKE DOUBLE & FREEZE.

If you like : Try adding chilli - fresh or powder*

1. Rinse & cook the lentils in plenty of boiling water until soft - about 30 minutes. Rinse & drain.

2. <u>Meanwhile</u> : Peel the vegetables & chop into small pieces. Wash & chop the spinach. Put aside.

3. Cover the bottom of a large pan with olive oil and add, in this order: potatoes, carrots, leeks, onions, garlic, ginger & cumin.(* Pinch of chilli powder or piece of fresh too)

4. Fry gently, stirring occasionally, for about 5 minutes. Add ¼ litre water, 1 tbs. bouillon or 1 stock cube.

5. Simmer until the potatoes are soft & then add the lentils and spinach. Bring to the boil. TURN OFF.

6. Stir in the miso, season & serve with basmati rice & sheets of toasted sushi nori. Filling & warming.

Aduki Bean & Sweet Potato Hotpot

250g aduki beans (dried)
500g onions
500g sweet potatoes
350g carrots
olive oil
4 cloves garlic
3 cm cube ginger root
1 tin chopped tomatoes
1 small tin tomato purée
vegetable bouillon or stock cube
tamari
medium bunch fresh coriander.

1. Soak the aduki beans overnight
2. Rinse beans & put in a large pan with plenty of water. Boil rapidly for 10 mins. & then simmer/slow boil for about 1 hour until the beans are soft. Drain & rinse.
3. Meanwhile : peel & chop the onions, carrots & sweet potatoes into 1 cm cubes.
4. Fry gently in enough olive oil to cover the bottom of a frying pan. Meanwhile peel & chop the ginger & garlic and add to the pan.
5. When the vegetables are soft, add the cooked beans, tomatoes and tomato purée. Stir in.
6. Add the tamari and vegetable stock cube or bouillon.
7. To serve : add the chopped coriander and eat with broccoli & rice or fresh crusty bread and salad.

(This FREEZES well)   Yummy!

Chickpea Rissoles

3 tins chickpeas (drained)
2 medium onions
500g peeled potatoes
4 cloves garlic
1 dsp. cumin powder
2 dsp. lemon juice
2 tbs. tamari
bowl of wholemeal flour
soya milk
250g of fresh breadcrumbs (you will need a food processor & slices of wholemeal bread)
Olive oil for frying.

1. Chop and boil the potatoes in a pan of water.
2. Meanwhile mash the chickpeas with a fork.
3. <u>Very finely</u> chop the onions & garlic and mix into the chick peas. Add the lemon juice, cumin, tamari & salt & plenty of freshly ground pepper. Mash, & add the potatoes.
4. Fill three bowls with ① Flour ② soya milk ③ breadcrumbs.
5. Roll the mixture into about 5cm (2½ in) balls & flatten, & then coat each one with ① flour, ② soya milk ③ breadcrumbs.
6. Fry for a few minutes on each side in ½ inch of olive oil in a non-stick frying pan.
7. Serve with spicy tomato sauce (page 42) & green leafy salad or steamed vegetables

QUITE A LOT OF PREPARATION SO MAKE SOME & FREEZE SOME. (UNFRIED)

Shepherdess Pie

375g soya mince (dried)
500g carrots (or 2 small)
1 large onion
1 large leek (or 2 small)
3 cloves garlic
500g swede
750g potatoes
1 small tin tomato purée
3 bay leaves
1 vegetable stock cube
Olive oil

1. Peel & cut potatoes in <u>2 cm</u> cubes. Peel & cut the swede in <u>1 cm</u> cubes. Boil together, starting in cold water.
2. Chop the carrots into very small cubes (peel if not organic). Peel & chop the onions, leek & garlic & fry gently in enough oil to cover the bottom of the pan. Meanwhile :
3. Make some stock: dissolve stock cube in 1 pint boiling water.* Add tomato purée & bay leaves.
4. Add the soya mince & stock to the vegetables & place in a casserole dish. Season with salt & pepper.
5. Drain & mash the potatoes & swede (You can add some soya milk & a blob of margarine). Season.
6. Put the mashed potato mix on top of the mince mix & brown the top in a hot oven (about ½ hour).
7. Serve with lots of broccoli and spring greens.

MAKE TWO & FREEZE ONE?
NB. If using frozen mince, only use ½ cup of water *

35

Vegetable Pasties

(makes 12)

400g self-raising flour
200g margarine
250g potatoes
250g carrots
200g leeks
250g onions
3 cloves garlic
100g red lentils
Olive oil
1 heaped tsp. bouillon.
salt & pepper

1. <u>Pastry</u> : Sieve the flour & salt into a bowl. Break the margarine into pieces and rub into the flour until the mixture is like breadcrumbs. (Do not over-handle pastry with warm hands!)

2. Make a well in the middle and slowly add water & mix in until the dough is soft but not sticky. Put in fridge.

3. Peel and chop the potatoes, carrots, leeks, onions & garlic. The vegetables should be in small ¼" (½ cm) cubes.

4. Fry the vegetables gently in enough olive oil to cover the bottom of a pan. When they soften, add 500 mL (1 pint) of cold water. Add the lentils and bring to the boil. When the lentils are soft add the bouillon. Season. Cool the mixture.

5. Roll the pastry dough out onto a floured surface until it is less than ½ cm (¼") thick. Cut into rounds of about 7" (18cm) in diameter. (Try a plate or saucer)

6. Put a big tablespoonful of mixture into the middle of each circle of pastry. Run some soya milk around the edge of the pastry and draw up the edges onto the top. Punch along.

7. Bake in a hot oven on a greased baking tray for about 35-40 mins. (Gas 6, , 200°C) until browned.

Vegetable Crumble

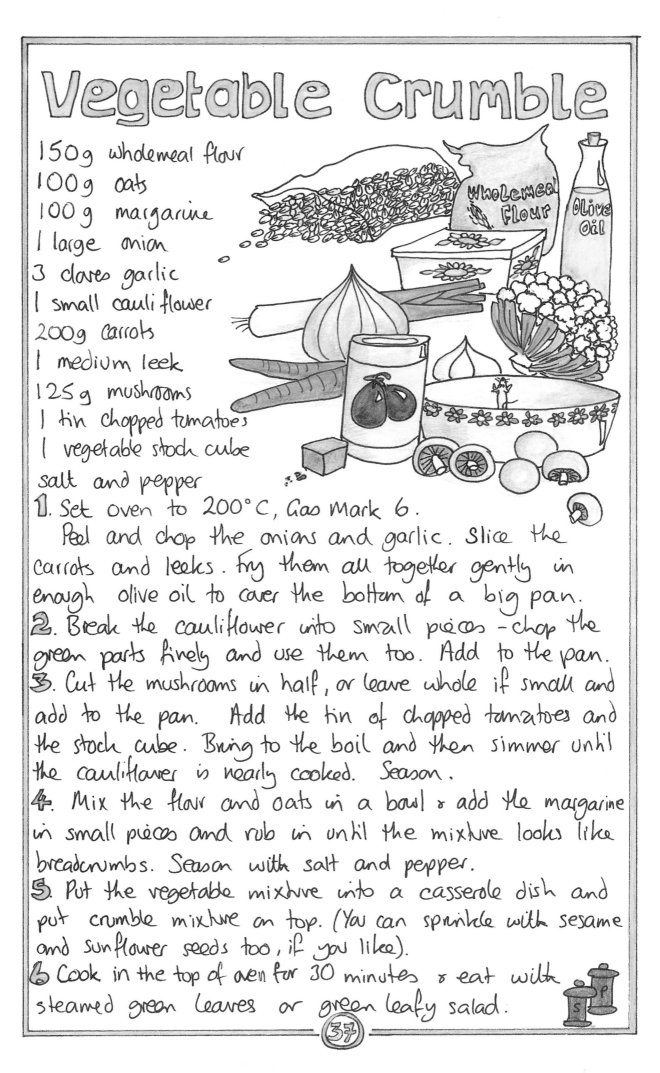

150g wholemeal flour
100g oats
100g margarine
1 large onion
3 cloves garlic
1 small cauliflower
200g carrots
1 medium leek
125g mushrooms
1 tin chopped tomatoes
1 vegetable stock cube
salt and pepper

1. Set oven to 200°C, Gas Mark 6.
   Peel and chop the onions and garlic. Slice the carrots and leeks. Fry them all together gently in enough olive oil to cover the bottom of a big pan.

2. Break the cauliflower into small pieces - chop the green parts finely and use them too. Add to the pan.

3. Cut the mushrooms in half, or leave whole if small and add to the pan. Add the tin of chopped tomatoes and the stock cube. Bring to the boil and then simmer until the cauliflower is nearly cooked. Season.

4. Mix the flour and oats in a bowl & add the margarine in small pieces and rub in until the mixture looks like breadcrumbs. Season with salt and pepper.

5. Put the vegetable mixture into a casserole dish and put crumble mixture on top. (You can sprinkle with sesame and sunflower seeds too, if you like).

6 Cook in the top of oven for 30 minutes & eat with steamed green leaves or green leafy salad.

SAVOURY PANCAKES

250g Wholemeal self-raising flour

2 tablespoons wine vinegar

2 dessertspoon sunflower oil

½ litre soya milk

salt & pepper

4 tsp dried herbs – eg: oregano;
  basil or fresh: coriander, parsley.

Olive oil for frying.

1. Sieve the flour into a bowl. Slowly whisk in the soya milk, oil, vinegar, herbs & salt & pepper. Chill for an hour. Before using, add a tablespoon of cold water and whisk again. (A hand-blender is useful for this)

2. Add a bit of oil to a small non-stick or heavy bottomed iron frying pan. Tip the pan around to cover the bottom with the oil.

3. When oil begins. to smoke add enough batter to cover the middle of the pan & tilt it around to spread the mixture out to the sides of the pan.

4. When the pancake bubbles (after 1-2 minutes) slide a palette knife around the edges, until the pancake lifts free. If the first one sticks, don't panic. Try again!

5. Turn the pancake over & cook the other side for a minute and slide the pancake out.

7. Serve with gravy & vegetables & roast potatoes, or fill them with ratatouille (p.43) or spicy tomato sauce (p.42) and french bread & salad.

(✰ If you leave out the herbs this is the recipe for 'sweet' pancakes too.)

PIZZAS

EASY BASE:

225g self-raising white flour
50g margarine
½ tsp salt
2 tbs. soya milk & 2 tbs. water

TOPPING:

½ tin chopped tomatoes
1 tsp dried mixed herbs
soya 'cheese' (optional)

+ CHOOSE FROM:

olives/fresh tomatoes/
vegan "rashers" or sausages
mushrooms/peppers/sliced onions
sweetcorn/courgettes (or anything .....)

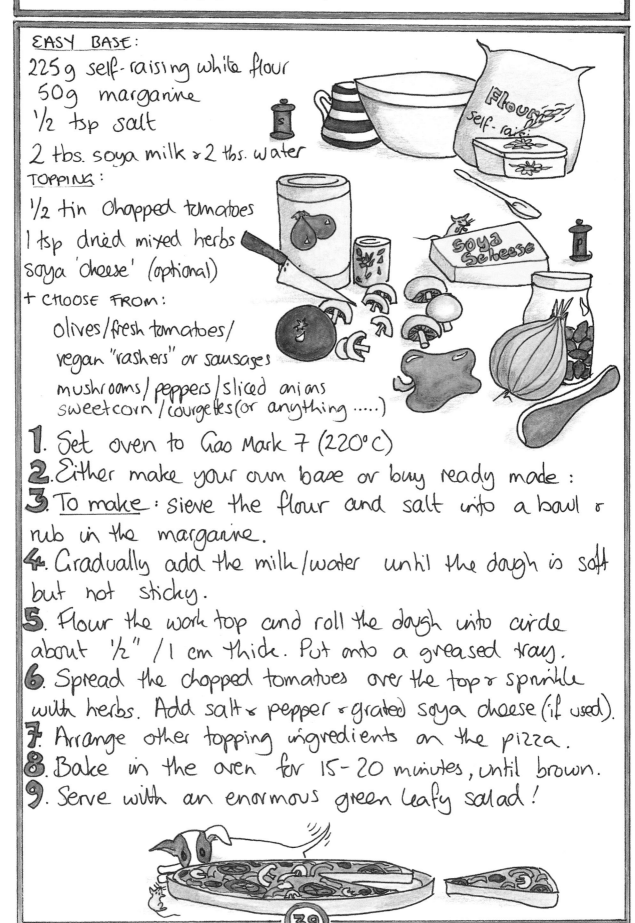

1. Set oven to Gas Mark 7 (220°c)
2. Either make your own base or buy ready made:
3. To make: sieve the flour and salt into a bowl & rub in the margarine.
4. Gradually add the milk/water until the dough is soft but not sticky.
5. Flour the work top and roll the dough into circle about ½"/1 cm thick. Put onto a greased tray.
6. Spread the chopped tomatoes over the top & sprinkle with herbs. Add salt & pepper & grated soya cheese (if used).
7. Arrange other topping ingredients on the pizza.
8. Bake in the oven for 15-20 minutes, until brown.
9. Serve with an enormous green leafy salad!

Lentil Roast

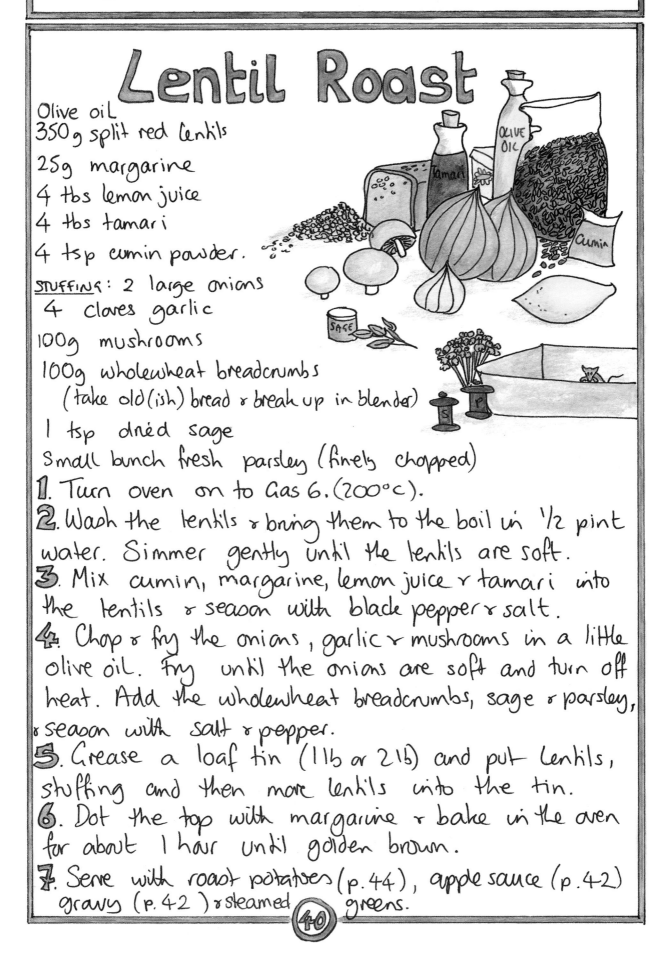

Olive oil
350g split red lentils
25g margarine
4 tbs lemon juice
4 tbs tamari
4 tsp cumin powder.
STUFFING: 2 large onions
 4 cloves garlic
100g mushrooms
100g wholewheat breadcrumbs
   (take old(ish) bread & break up in blender)
1 tsp dried sage
Small bunch fresh parsley (finely chopped)

1. Turn oven on to Gas 6. (200°c).
2. Wash the lentils & bring them to the boil in ½ pint water. Simmer gently until the lentils are soft.
3. Mix cumin, margarine, lemon juice & tamari into the lentils & season with black pepper & salt.
4. Chop & fry the onions, garlic & mushrooms in a little olive oil. Fry until the onions are soft and turn off heat. Add the wholewheat breadcrumbs, sage & parsley, & season with salt & pepper.
5. Grease a loaf tin (1lb or 2lb) and put lentils, stuffing and then more lentils into the tin.
6. Dot the top with margarine & bake in the oven for about 1 hour until golden brown.
7. Serve with roast potatoes (p.44), apple sauce (p.42) gravy (p.42) & steamed greens.

Cashew Loaf

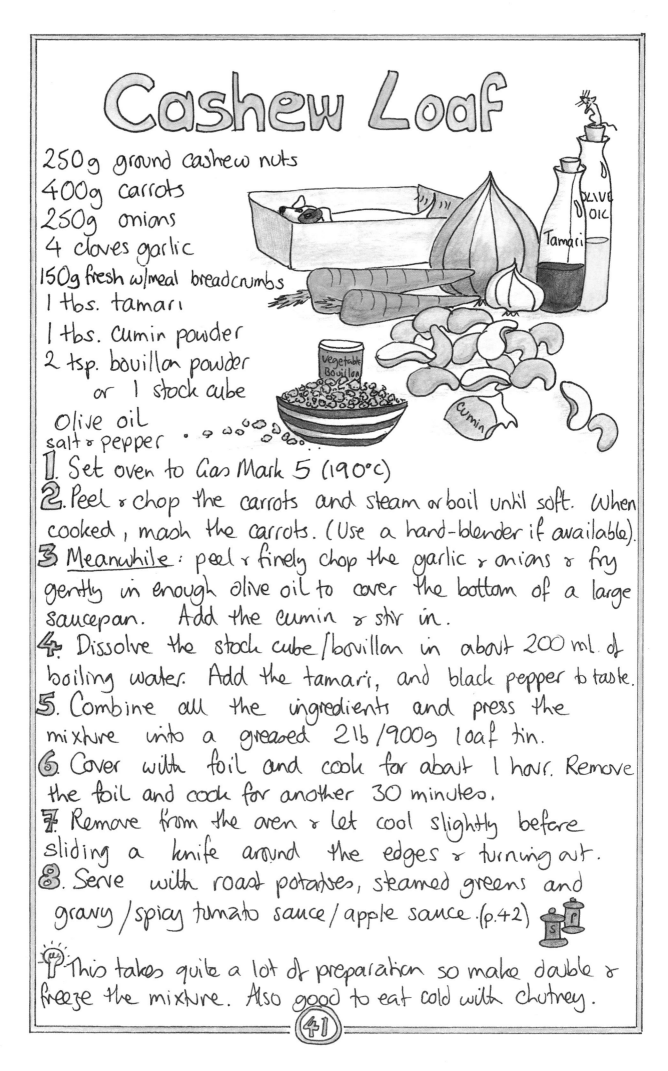

250g ground cashew nuts
400g carrots
250g onions
4 cloves garlic
150g fresh w/meal breadcrumbs
1 tbs. tamari
1 tbs. cumin powder
2 tsp. bouillon powder
    or 1 stock cube
Olive oil
salt & pepper

1. Set oven to Gas Mark 5 (190°C)
2. Peel & chop the carrots and steam or boil until soft. When cooked, mash the carrots. (Use a hand-blender if available).
3. Meanwhile: peel & finely chop the garlic & onions & fry gently in enough olive oil to cover the bottom of a large saucepan. Add the cumin & stir in.
4. Dissolve the stock cube/bouillon in about 200 ml. of boiling water. Add the tamari, and black pepper to taste.
5. Combine all the ingredients and press the mixture into a greased 2lb/900g loaf tin.
6. Cover with foil and cook for about 1 hour. Remove the foil and cook for another 30 minutes.
7. Remove from the oven & let cool slightly before sliding a knife around the edges & turning out.
8. Serve with roast potatoes, steamed greens and gravy/spicy tomato sauce/apple sauce.(p.42)

This takes quite a lot of preparation so make double & freeze the mixture. Also good to eat cold with chutney.

Apple Sauce

Cooking apples eg: Bramleys
brown sugar

1. Peel, core and slice the apples. Put
in a pan with a little bit of water r the sugar
2. Cook until the apples are soft, stirring all
the time. Mash up.

Spicy Tomato Sauce

some olive oil
1 onion
1 tin chopped tomatoes
1 clove garlic
½ small tin tom. purée
1 tbsp. tamari
(few drops of tabasco)

1. Chop r fry the onions r garlic gently in a little
olive oil. Add the other ingredients. Bring to the boil.
2. and blend. Add tabasco if you like it hot! Season.

Gravy

1 stock cube
   cornflour
   water (from steamed veg).
1. Mix the cornflour into
a paste with a little cold water.
2. Dissolve the stock cube in the boiling water* and
add slowly to the cornflour paste. Return to the pan r
bring back to the boil. 42 Season with salt r pepper.

Ratatouille

(no rats...)

1 large onion
4 cloves garlic
2 medium courgettes
1 large aubergine
1 red pepper
1 green pepper
1 dsp. tomato purée.
1 tin chopped tomatoes
  oregano - dried or fresh
  salt & pepper

1. Peel and chop the onions and garlic and fry gently in enough olive oil to cover the bottom of a large pan.

2. Chop the courgettes, aubergines and peppers and add to the pan. Put the lid on and cook gently until the aubergine is soft.

3. Add the tomatoes and tomato purée and cook slowly for a few more minutes.

4. Chop the oregano if fresh and add to the pan. Or add the dried herbs. Season with salt & lots of fresh ground pepper. Simmer with the lid on for another ten minutes.

5. Use the ratatouille as a vegetable, as a pasta sauce or filling for jacket potatoes. Good the next day!

← not a rat ...

Roast Potatoes

1 large potato per peson
Olive oil
salt + pepper

1. Pre-heat oven to Gas 7,(220°C)
2. Peel and chop the potatoes into
5cm (2") pieces.
3. Put the potatoes into a pan of cold water and bring
to the boil. Cook the potatoes until they <u>begin</u> to soften.
4. Drain the potatoes. Cover the roasting tin bottom with
olive oil + heat in the oven. Add the potatoes.
5. Roast in the oven, turning the potatoes over once or twice
until golden brown.(About 45 minutes.)   Yum yum!

Roasted Root Vegetables

1 beetroot (large)
½ swede
2 parsnips
4 carrots
1 sprig fresh rosemary
Olive oil
salt + pepper

1. Pre-heat the oven to Gas 7, 220°C.
2. Peel and chop the vegetables into approx. 1"/2½cm
pieces and put them into a roasting tin with enough
olive oil to cover the bottom of the tin. Sprinkle with herbs.
3. Cook for about 1 hour, turning the vegetables over
once or twice. Season.

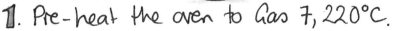

Homemade Chips

1 medium potato / person
olive oil
kitchen paper
Tomato sauce
(see p.42)
salt

1. If using organic potatoes, just wash and chop.
2. Fry in enough olive oil to ½ cover the chips and keep turning until golden brown. Drain on kitchen paper.
3. Serve with tomato sauce – home-made or bottled.

Jacket Potatoes

1 large potato per person
Filling

1. Skewer potatoes on metal skewers or wrap in silver foil and cook in a medium oven until soft.
2. Split open and fill with hummus, soya cheese, baked beans, shepherdess pie filling or ratatouille.

Steamed Vegetables

The best way to cook vegetables to keep the nutrients in! Layer them up: carrots, swede, broccoli, greens ...

SALADS

There are really no rules about salads - you can put just about any combination of the following things together with french dressing, egg-free mayonnaise or (really good) just olive or sesame oil, a bit of lemon or lime juice and a little salt. Experiment!

some salad ingredients:

○ Green leaves - lettuces eg: radiccio, oak leaf, cos, ice-berg, chinese leaves, young-leaf spinach, flat-leaf parsley, basil, coriander, rocket, lambs lettuce, green, red and white cabbage.

○ Cucumber, celery, tomatoes, avocado, olives, garlic.

○ Sundried tomatoes (see p.50).

○ Mushrooms (raw), small florets of broccoli, cauliflower

○ Beetroot, peppers, beansprouts (p.50.)

○ Cooked potato, grated carrots.

○ Fruit - apples, oranges, grapes, raisins.

○ Nuts & seeds: toasted sesame, pumpkin & sunflower seeds (p.51). Cashew, hazelnuts, walnuts & brazils.

○ Cooked grains : rice, pasta, millet, cous-cous, bulgar wheat.

○ Tins - sweetcorn, kidney beans, flageolet beans, chick peas.

○ Soya or other egg-free mayonnaise, vinaigrette.

Try organic...

Pink Potato Salad

500g cooked potatoes (new are good)
3-4 spring onions
Small bunches of dill, chives
  & parsley - (one or more)
4 tablespoons soya mayonnaise
1 small cooked beetroot
Salt & pepper

1. Chop the cooked potatoes into 2½ cm cubes. Finely chop the herbs and spring onions.
(1 inch)
2. Peel and dice the beetroot. Add to the potatoes. (This is good without beetroot too).
3. Add the soya mayonnaise & season with salt & freshly ground black pepper.

Pasta Salad

250g pasta shapes (eg shells)
100g frozen peas
1 small tin sweetcorn
½ red pepper - chopped
One or more of: fresh basil,
  oregano, basil and coriander
½ large avocado - chopped
100g black olives
4 tbs soya mayonnaise.

1. Cook the pasta. Add the peas at the last minute. Drain. Chop the herbs.
2. Mix everything together. Salt, pepper.

Rice Salad

350g cooked wholegrain rice
50g cashew nuts
100g toasted seeds (see p.51)
2 or 3 spring onions
100g beansprouts (p.50)
small bunch fresh herbs:
    one or more: Coriander/basil
    oregano, parsley.
6 tablespoons vinaigrette (p.51).

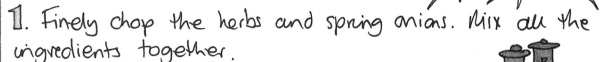

1. Finely chop the herbs and spring onions. Mix all the ingredients together.
2. Season with salt & pepper. Yummy!

Coleslaw

350g white cabbage
350g carrots
1 apple
2 sticks celery
2 tablespoons sunflower seeds
2 tbs. nuts (eg brazils (chopped)
    hazelnuts, cashews)
2 tbs. raisins.
4 big tablespoons soya mayonnaise.

1. Grate the carrots, finely slice the cabbage and chop the apple & celery into small pieces.
2. Mix everything together & season with salt & pepper.

Chickpeas & Garlic

(SO SIMPLE!)

1 tin chickpeas
3 cloves garlic
1 tbs. fresh lemon juice
small bunch herbs –
(one or more) basil / parsley / coriander.
Olive oil
salt and pepper.

Try: adding some cubes of avocado and/or strips of sundried tomatoes. Lots of fresh ground pepper. Mmm...
(see p. 50)

1. Rinse and drain the chick peas. Chop the garlic and herbs finely.
2. Mix all the ingredients together, using enough olive oil to coat the chick peas. Eat with warm toast or pitta bread and green leafy salad.

Green Leaf Salad with Toasted Seeds

Selection of green salad leaves (p. 46)
2 tbs. toasted seeds (p. 51)
4-5 tbs. vinaigrette (p. 51).

1. Wash all the leaves and arrange in a glass bowl.
2. Drizzle over with the vinaigrette & sprinkle with the toasted seeds. Lovely!

Beansprouts

HOW TO SPROUT THEM (- EASY!)

½ cup of mung beans or alfalfa seeds
Jars with holes in the lid.

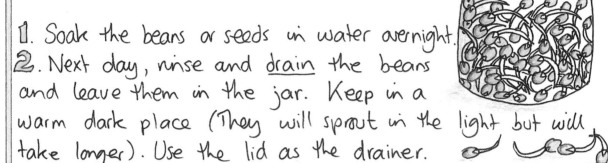

1. Soak the beans or seeds in water overnight.
2. Next day, rinse and <u>drain</u> the beans and leave them in the jar. Keep in a warm dark place (They will sprout in the light but will take longer). Use the lid as the drainer.
3. Rinse & drain each day. After 3 days you will have a jar of delicious, vitamin-packed beansprouts.
4. Keep the beansprouts in an airtight box in the fridge.

Sundried Tomatoes

½ packet of sundried tomatoes
Olive oil
3 cloves garlic
small bunch fresh herbs :
     basil /coriander/ oregano
Lemon juice - about 1 tbs.

1. Soak the dried tomatoes in boiling water for about 1 hour until soft.
2. Drain the tomatoes and add enough olive oil to coat the tomatoes. Add the chopped garlic, chopped herbs, lemon juice and salt and pepper to taste. Keep in an airtight box in the fridge & use in everything! (well almost...) Seriously yummy.

Vinaigrette

²/₃ cup extra virgin olive oil
¹/₃ cup white wine vinegar
1 tsp. grainy mustard
1 tsp. rice syrup or brown sugar.
1 clove garlic, crushed
1 dessert spoon nutritional yeast
    (flakes or powder) - optional.

1. Mix ingredients together in a jar with a lid. Season with salt and pepper.
2. Store in the fridge and shake each time you use it. (This is also called French Dressing)

Toasted Seeds

½ cup of sesame seeds
½ cup of sunflower seeds
½ cup of pumpkin seeds
tamari
Olive oil

Method 1.: Put the seeds on a baking tray with a little tamari and olive oil. Mix well and bake in the oven for about 10 minutes until brown. ✱
Method 2: Do the same but grill the seeds, turning them over all the time. ✱
Method 3.: Fry the seeds gently in the oil & tamari. ✱

    ✱ DO NOT LET THEM BURN!

Stuffed Pitta Bread

1 pitta bread per peson
Choose from :
Fried mushrooms, tofu, (p.28)
soya bacon.
cherry tomatoes,
beansprouts, cucumber,
salad leaves, hummous,
soya mayonnaise ...

1. Split the pitta breads down the middle and heat under the grill, in the toaster or in the oven.
2. Pile in loads of different ingredients!   Eat!

Sandwiches

Savoury: Yeast extract, beansprouts & lettuce.
: Hummous (page 53) and tomato.
: Vegetarian pâté with cucumber.
: Tahini and coleslaw. (see p.48)
: Soya bacon, lettuce and tomato with
   soya mayonnaise (B.L.T. - yum!).
  Try: Drizzling olive oil onto bread instead of margarine

Sweet: Tahini and pear-and-apple-spread
  : Cashew and almond butters with jam
  : Banana and the above...
N.B.: Organic wholemeal bread is best!

Hummous Dip

1 tin (225g) chick peas
4 tbs. olive oil
2 cloves garlic
4 tbs lemon juice
1 tbs. tahini
Ground black pepper
salt.

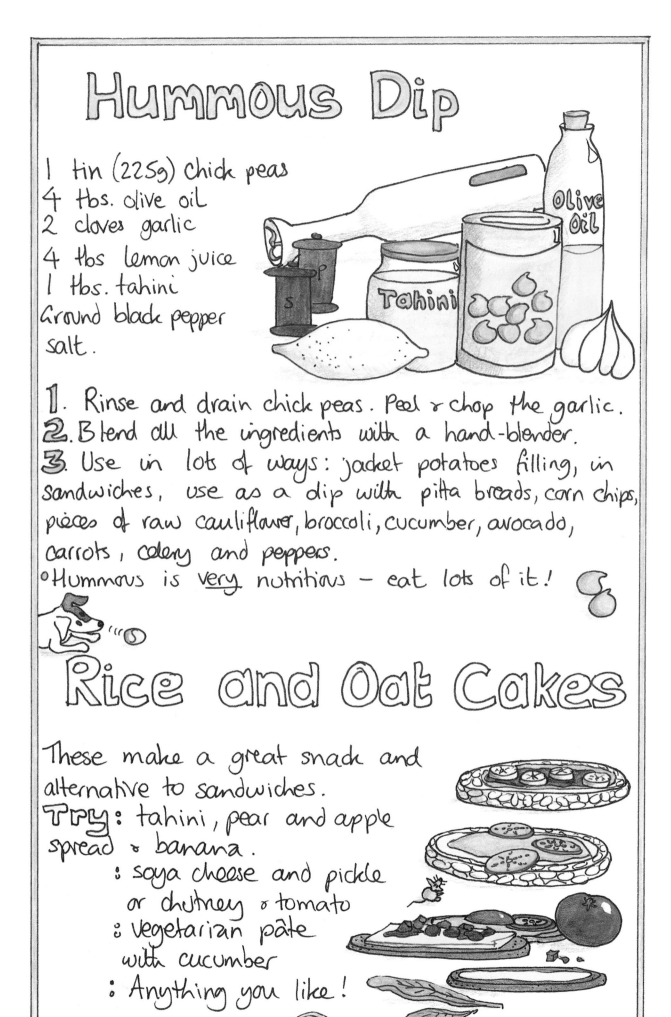

1. Rinse and drain chick peas. Peel & chop the garlic.
2. Blend all the ingredients with a hand-blender.
3. Use in lots of ways: jacket potatoes filling, in sandwiches, use as a dip with pitta breads, corn chips, pieces of raw cauliflower, broccoli, cucumber, avocado, carrots, celery and peppers.
° Hummous is <u>very</u> nutritious — eat lots of it!

Rice and Oat Cakes

These make a great snack and alternative to sandwiches.
Try: tahini, pear and apple spread & banana.
: soya cheese and pickle or chutney & tomato
: vegetarian pâté with cucumber
: Anything you like!

Beans on Toast plus...

Yes! They really are a good nutritious meal. Try and use wholemeal bread r even try some organic beans...
Add : Vegetarian sausages*, soya bacon, smoked tofu or marinated tempeh.
Add : Something green : some salad or steamed broccoli. Quick r easy!

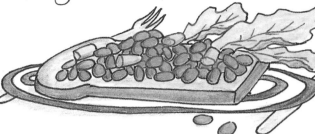

Hot Dogs

1 hot dog roll per peson
1 vegetarian sausage* per peson
Salad stuff : lettuce, tomato, cucumber, Ketchup and Mustard.
1. Cook the sausages according to instructions.
2. Pile everything into the bread roll r eat!

Veggie Burgers

1 burger bap per peson
1 veggie burger* per peson
1 fried onion, sliced r fried
            in olive oil.
Salad stuff : tomatoes, lettuce, cucumber.
Mustard and tomato ketchup.
1. Prepare as for hot-dogs.

* Check for animal-free ones

Vanilla Sponge

250g self-raising flour
85 ml. sunflower oil
170 ml. maple or
     golden syrup
170 ml. soya milk &
     water (mixed).
2 tsp. vanilla essence
1 dsp. wine vinegar
Jar of jam

1. Set the oven to Gas Mark 5, (190°C)·
2. Sieve the flour into a bowl.
3. Whisk the syrup, oil, milk & water, vinegar & vanilla essence in a jug. Pour slowly into the flour & stir in well.
4. Grease an 8" or 9" cake tin and pour in the mixture. Cook in the oven for about 40 minutes until a sharp knife comes out clean.
5. When cooked, cool & tip the cake out. Cut in half across the middle & spread with jam. (You can shake a bit of icing sugar (through a sieve) onto the top).
6. To make a fatter cake — double the mixture, cook in two tins & sandwich together.
7. Try covering the bottom of the tin with thin slices of apple and adding cinammon (1 tsp) to the cake mixture, to make an apple cake.

Chocolate Cake

170g self-raising wholemeal flour
170g self-raising white flour
6 dsp. cocoa powder
220 mL. maple syrup
2 tsp. vanilla essence
12 dsp. sunflower oil
450 ml soya milk

1. Turn oven on to 180°C (Gas Mark 4.)
2. Sift the flour (x2) and cocoa powder into a bowl.
3. In another bowl, whisk the sunflower oil, soya milk maple syrup and vanilla essence.
4. Pour the liquid ingredients bit by bit into the flour and cocoa, whisking gently to make a batter.
5. Wipe some oil around two 20cm (8") cake tins, & sprinkle some flour in the bottom. Tap the flour around to cover the tin. (This will help the cake come out.)
6. Put half the mixture into each tin & cook for about 40 minutes until a sharp knife comes out cleanly.
7. Cool slightly and loosen the edges with a knife. Turn the cakes out & when cold sandwich together with chocolate butter-icing. Decorate the top with with icing and dark chocolate curls (use a grater).

Chocolate Butter Icing

75g margarine ⎫ Beat together thoroughly with a
75g icing sugar ⎬ dessertspoon of boiling water. (You can
75g cocoa powder ⎭ use a hand blender) Mmm...

"Cut and Come Again" Loaf

(THIS IS INCREDIBLY QUICK & EASY. A NUTRITIOUS & YUMMY
TEA-LOAF)

1 mug bran cereal (eg: "Allbran")
1 mug self-raising wholemeal flour
1 mug soya milk
1 mug dried fruit
1 tablespoon brown sugar

1. Soak the bran cereal in the milk for a couple of mins.
2. Add the fruit, flour and sugar. Mix well.
3. Grease a small (1lb) loaf tin, put mixture in and bake in the oven (Gas Mark 4, 180°C) for about 1 - 1¼ hours - it is cooked when a sharp knife comes out clean.

💡 There are lots of variations of this. Try some of the following and experiment too!

Try: Soaked dates, chopped dried figs, sunflower seeds, raisins, sultanas as part of the mug of dried fruit.

Try: A mug full of mashed banana instead of the fruit to make banana bread.

Try: Blackstrap molasses, golden syrup, maple syrup, or rice syrup instead of sugar.

Try: sprinkling a handful of sesame seeds on top before baking.

Apple Pie

200g plain flour
　　　(white or wholemeal)
100g margarine
a little cold water
pinch of salt
450g cooking apples
　　　　　eg Bramley
50g soft brown sugar.

1. Set oven to Gas Mark 6 , (200°C)
2. Sieve the flour & salt into a bowl.
3. Rub the margarine in to the flour until the mixture looks like fine breadcrumbs. Make a well in the middle & slowly add water until mixture stays together but isn't sticky.
4. Don't handle too much, and then put in fridge.
5. Meanwhile: peel, core and thinly slice the apples.
6. Roll the pastry out to about ½cm thick on a floured surface. Cut out a circle big enough to cover the bottom & sides of an 8" pie dish. Bake for 10 mins.
7. Take out of oven and put apples onto pastry base. Sprinkle with sugar. Cover top with another circle of pastry. Seal up the edges with soya milk. Brush top with milk & pierce top with a knife.
8. Bake for another 20-25 minutes until pastry golden. Serve with soya custard or soya ice-cream.

★ In the autumn, add some **blackberries** to the apples.

Fruit Crumble

2 pears
2 bananas
110g dried apricots
1 orange
250g wholemeal r white
   flour mixed
2 dsp. brown sugar (soft)
100g margarine

1. Set oven to Gas Mark 7, 220°C.
2. Soak the apricots in boiling water for 30 minutes r meanwhile: peel, core r slice the pears. Arrange on the bottom of an oven dish (approx 20 cm. round).
3. Peel the orange and chop up. Peel and chop the bananas. Put in the dish.
4. Sieve the flour into a bowl and rub in the margarine until the mixture looks like fine breadcrumbs. Stir in the sugar.
5. Chop the apricots and add to the fruit.
6. Lay the crumble mix on top of the fruit and press down very firmly.
7. Cook in the oven for 30 minutes until the top is golden brown. Serve with soja icecream, custard or banana cream. A good, hot winter pudding !

Variations: Try adding different things to the crumble: sesame seeds, oats, crushed nuts, dried coconut, and different fruit: apples, plums, raspberries, pineapple or peaches.   Very versatile dish!

Upside-down Pudding

1 small tin pineapple rings
2 tbs golden syrup
Glacé cherries (or fresh)
250g self-raising flour
85 ml. sunflower oil
170 ml. maple syrup
170 ml. soya milk
1 dessert spoon wine vinegar
2 tsp vanilla essence

1. Turn oven on to Gas 5, (190°C)
2. Whisk together the oil, maple syrup, soya milk, wine vinegar and vanilla essence
3. Sieve flour into a bowl and gradually pour in the liquid, stirring all the time.
4. Grease a shallow casserole dish or flan dish (about 9" (23cm)). Arrange the pineapple rings on the bottom and put ½ a cherry in the middle of each one. Pour the golden syrup over the pineapple and then the cake mixture over the top.
5. Bake in the oven for about 40-45 minutes until a sharp knife comes out clean.
6. Cool slightly & then put a plate over the top & turn the whole thing over. The cake will 'plop' neatly out onto the plate. We hope...! Serve with soya cream, ice-cream or custard.
Mmm...Gooey!

Fruit Salad

1 large orange
1 large apple
2 bananas
small bunch grapes
1 pear
2 kiwi fruits
apple juice concentrate
½ lemon juice

Then choose extra things from :
   raspberries, strawberries, plums
   peaches, melons, cherries

1. Wash or peel, chop and remove pips and stones. Cut all the fruit into nearly equal size pieces.
2. Add the lemon juice and drizzle over a bit of apple juice concentrate. Mix well & chill in the fridge.
3. Serve with soya cream or soya ice-cream.   Yum-yum!

Mango Hedgehog

This is a fun way of eating mango. Mangoes are full of vitamin C and delicious. Power food!
1. Cut the mango down each side of the long thin stone. 2. Cut criss-cross with a sharp knife through to (but not through) the skin. 3. Turn inside - out!

1.

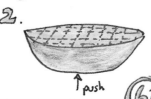
2.
↑push

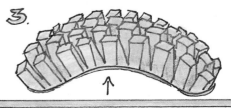
3.
↑

Rice Pudding

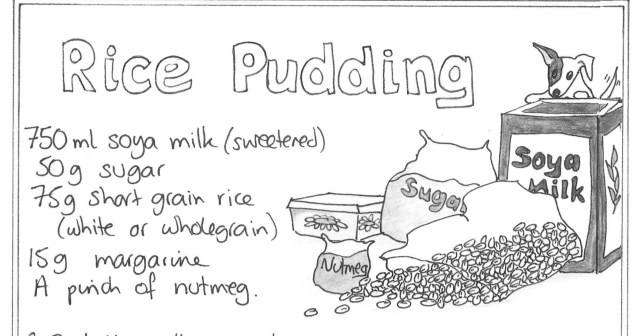

750 ml soya milk (sweetened)
50 g sugar
75 g short grain rice
   (white or wholegrain)
15 g margarine
A pinch of nutmeg.

1. Boil the milk in a heavy-bottomed pan.
2. Wash the rice and add to the pan – stir in.
3. Bring back to the boil, simmer gently, stirring frequently until the rice is completely soft – 15 mins for white rice, about 40 minutes for wholegrain rice.
4. Add the sugar, nutmeg and margarine & stir in.
Try: Adding a tablespoon of cocoa powder to the milk & whisk in, to make chocolate rice pudding.
Try: Adding a handful of sultanas 10 minutes before the end of the simmering.

Custard

Custard powder (tin or packet)
Soya milk
sugar.

Soya milk makes perfect custard! Just follow the instructions on the packet, (they may vary).
Try: a dessertspoon of cocoa powder with the custard powder to make chocolate custard.

Fruit Scones

(MAKES 12)

225g plain white flour
225g wholemeal self-raising flour
½ tsp. salt
2 tsp. baking powder
40g sugar (optional)
100g margarine
250g sweetened soya milk
110g raisins or sultanas ✻

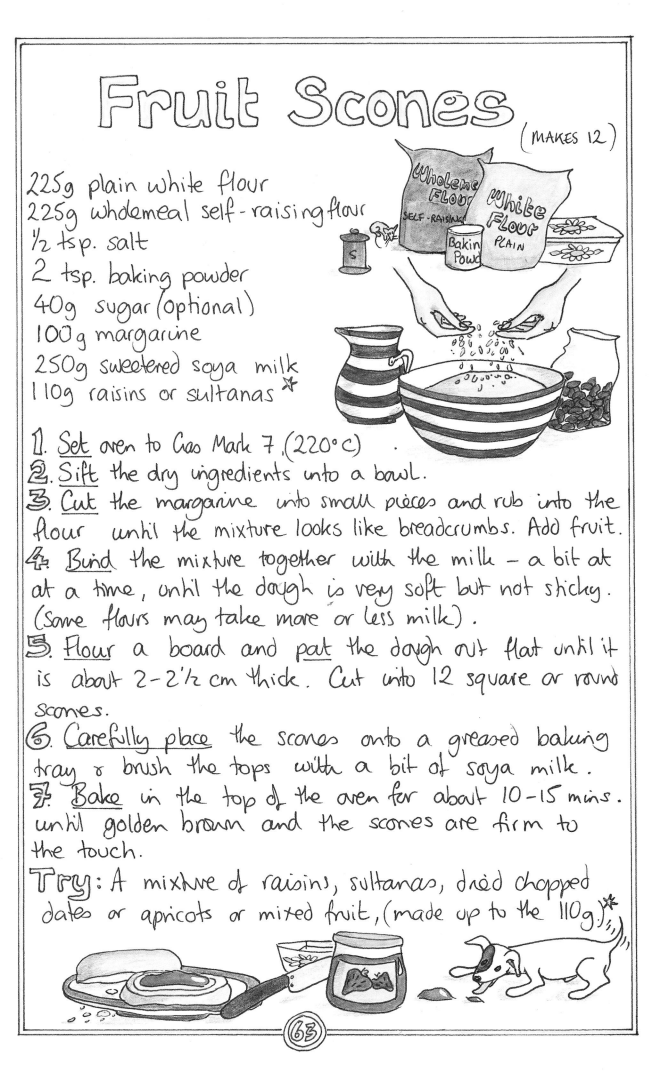

1. Set oven to Gas Mark 7, (220°c)
2. Sift the dry ingredients into a bowl.
3. Cut the margarine into small pieces and rub into the flour until the mixture looks like breadcrumbs. Add fruit.
4. Bind the mixture together with the milk — a bit at at a time, until the dough is very soft but not sticky. (Some flours may take more or less milk).
5. Flour a board and pat the dough out flat until it is about 2-2½ cm thick. Cut into 12 square or round scones.
6. Carefully place the scones onto a greased baking tray & brush the tops with a bit of soya milk.
7. Bake in the top of the oven for about 10-15 mins. until golden brown and the scones are firm to the touch.

Try: A mixture of raisins, sultanas, dried chopped dates or apricots or mixed fruit, (made up to the 110g). ✻

Flapjacks

EASY! (MAKES 12)

200g margarine
1 dsp. blackstrap molasses
150 g golden syrup or rice syrup
400 g rolled oats
mixed to 100 g * { sunflower seeds
sultanas
chopped cashew nuts
1 tsp. vanilla essence.

1. Set oven to Gas Mark 4, 350°F, 180°C.
2. Melt the margarine in a large saucepan.
3. Add the golden syrup r blackstrap molasses and dissolve gently. Add the vanilla essence
4. Gradually stir in the oats, sunflower seeds, sultanas and cashew nuts. Mix well.
5. Brush a 20cm x 30cm baking tray with oil and press the oat mixture down firmly into the tray. Bake in the oven for about 35 minutes until the top is lightly browned.
6. When cooked, allow to cool slightly and then cut into 12 pieces. Leave to cool completely r then remove from the baking tray.

Try: different things to make up to 100g * – chopped dates, chopped apricots, sesame seeds, currants, raisins, chopped almonds, hazelnuts, brazils....

Home-made Jelly

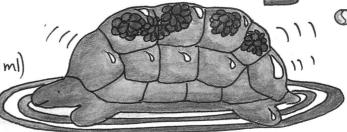

- agar-agar
- fruit juice (500ml)
- fresh fruit (100g)

1. Dissolve the agar-agar powder into 50 mL. of boiling water. (Follow amounts on packet, as they vary)

2. Add the fruit juice and bring gently to the boil, stirring all the time until it thickens

3. Lay fresh fruit (to match the juice if possible) eg: raspberries, apricots, mango, apple... & pour the juice over. Leave to set. (NB. Very acid juice may not set).

4. When set, run under hot water & tip out!

Baked Bananas

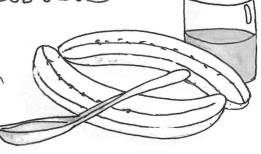

1 large ripe banana per person
70 ml. orange juice per person
½ tsp. brown sugar per person

1. Peel & slice the banana lengthways & lay in a dish.

2. Pour over the juice & sugar. Bake in a hot oven until soft & brown. Eat with soya ice-cream. Mmm...

Banana Cream

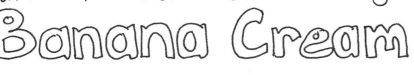

2 large ripe bananas
150 mL. soya milk
½ tsp. maple syrup

1. Blend all the ingredients together. Chill in fridge. Pour over puddings & fruit...

Sweet Ideas

Chocolate Fruit and nuts:

1 large bar black chocolate
pieces of banana
strawberries
brazils, cashews & almonds

Melt the chocolate in a bowl over a pan of boiling water (don't get water in the bowl). Dip the fruit & nuts in & leave to set on a greased tray.

Home-made Ice-Lollies:

Mashed fruit eg bananas, strawberries or raspberries
OR: Fresh fruit juice
OR: Soya yoghurts

You will need to have a lolly-mould (available in most supermarkets/hardware shops.) Simply fill & freeze!

Popcorn:

Pop your own in a little oil in a heavy bottom pan. Keep the lid on & shake until popping stops. Pop with sugar in the oil for sweet popcorn.

Drinks

o **Milk shakes** are great with soya milk, soft fruit, & a blob of soya-ice cream. Just whizz up in a blender.

o **Fizzy Juice** is easy: just mix pure juice concentrate with fizzy mineral water for a sugar-free version.

o **Hot Chocolate**: Soya milk & an instant dairy-free hot chocolate powder: perfect!

Conversion Charts

Weights

Ounces → grams.

¼ oz.	=	7g
½ oz.	=	14g
1 oz	=	28g
2 oz	=	56g
4 oz	=	115g
6 oz	=	170g
8 oz	=	225g
16 oz (1 lb)	=	450g

U.S. Cups:

Butter /Sugar/ Margarine :

Cups → Grams

¼	=	55g
½	=	115g
1	=	225g

Flour /Confectioners sugar :

Cups → Grams

¼	=	30g
½	=	60g
1	=	110g

Liquids

(1 fluid ounce = 28 mL.)
(1 cup (U.S.) = 230 mL)

140 mL.	=	¼ pint	=	5 fluid ounces
285 mL.	=	½ pint	=	10 fl. oz.
425 mL.	=	¾ pint	=	15 fl. oz.
570 mL.	=	1 pt.	=	20 fl. oz.
850 mL.	=	1½ pts.	=	30 fl. oz.
1·1 litres	=	2 pts.	=	40 fl. oz.

Oven

Gas →	°C →	°F
1	140	275
2	150	300
3	170	325
4	180	350
5	190	375
6	200	400
7	220	425

Spoons

1 tsp. =
1 teaspoon   5 mL.

1 dsp. =
1 dessertspoon   10 mL.

1 tbsp. =
1 tablespoon   15 mL.

"All you need" Shopping List !

(A list of all food & ingredients used in recipes & nutrition guides).

Fruit
Apricots
apples
bananas
blackcurrants
cherries
Kiwi fruit
lemons
mangoes
melons
grapes
peaches
plums
raspberries
strawberries
oranges
pears

Dried Fruit
sultanas
raisins
dates
apricots
figs
prunes

Salad Stuff
avocados
cucumber
tomatoes
beansprouts
celery
lettuces
young leaf spinach
watercress
spring onions
rocket

Herbs & Spices
Parsley
coriander
basil
bay leaves
oregano
sage
rosemary
ginger
chilli
cumin
nutmeg

Vegetables
Potatoes
leeks
onions
carrots
garlic
cabbage
spinach
kale
spring greens
chard
parsnips
swede
broccoli
cauliflower
peppers (-yellow green & red)
mushrooms
french beans
runner beans
courgettes
aubergines
beetroot
sweet potatoes.

Grains
cereals
rice : long and short wholegrain basmati, arborio
oats
millet
pearl barley
pasta
noodles
rice noodles
wholemeal bread
wholemeal flour
wheatgerm
pitta bread
oat cakes
rice cakes
popping corn

Nuts & Seeds
sunflower seeds
pumpkin seeds
sesame seeds
cashew nuts
hazelnuts
walnuts
brazils
almonds
pine kernels

Convenience
TINS: sweetcorn
baked beans
tinned tomatoes
tomato purée
coconut milk
chick peas
kidney beans
flageolet beans
FROZEN: Peas
veggie sausages
veggie burgers
soya mince
soya ice-cream
CHILLED:
soya yoghurt
soya cheese
soya mayonnaise
margarine
vegan pesto (jar)
hummous
orange juice
sundried tomato paste
tempeh
miso
creamed basil (jar)
tofu
pure juice concentrate
nut butters : eg:
cashew/peanut
tomato ketchup.

Pulses
Red lentils
green lentils
aduki beans
butterbeans
flageolet beans
haricot beans
pinto beans
chick peas
mung beans

Store-Cupboard
Extra-virgin oils
tamari
yeast extract
Veg. stock cubes.
veg. bouillon
olives (jar)
mustard
cider vinegar
dried soya mince 'sosmix'
'burgamix'
soya milk
nori, dulse, kelp
blackstrap molasses
tahini
nutritional yeast
green curry paste
pickle/chutney
cornflour
black pepper
sea salt
cocoa powder
soft brown sugar
agar-agar
custard powder
soya cream
soya dessert
vanilla essence
rice, maple & golden syrup
sugar-free jam & marmalade
pear 'n apple spread
baking powder

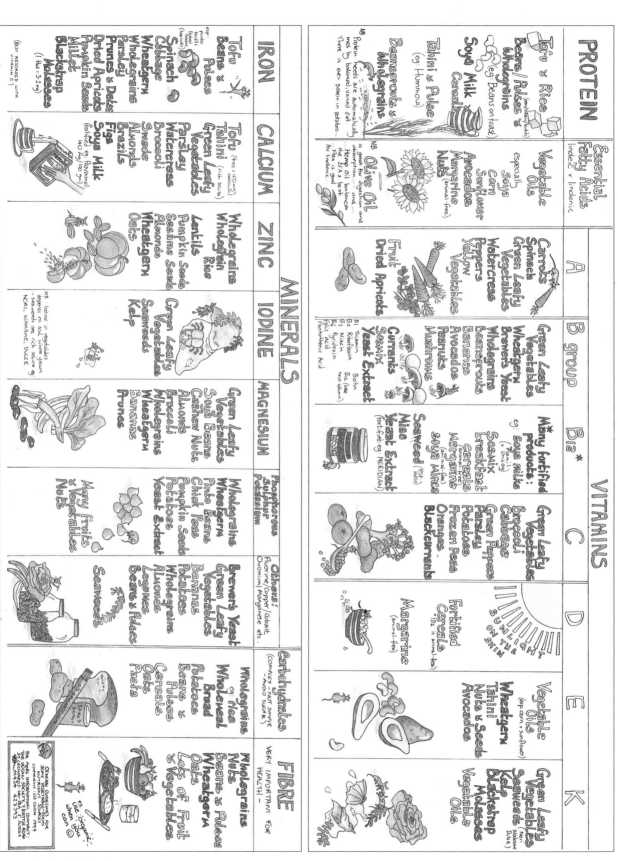

PROTEIN

- Tofu & Rice (complementary protein)
- Beans / Pulses & Wholegrains (eg Beans on toast)
- Soya Milk, Cereals
- Tahini & Pulse (eg Hummous)
- Beansprouts & Wholegrains

NB: Protein needs are automatically met by balanced / varied diet. There is even protein in potatoes.

Essential Fatty Acids (linoleic & linolenic)
- Vegetable Oils, especially Soya, Corn, Sunflower
- Avocados
- Margarine (animal-free)
- Nuts

NB: Olive Oil is great for digestion and... Hemp Oil balances the EFAs best. Flax is good for linolenic.

VITAMINS

A
- Carrots, Spinach, Green Leafy Vegetables, Watercress, Peppers, Yellow Vegetables
- Fruit, Dried Apricots

B group
- Green Leafy Vegetables, Wheatgerm, Brewer's Yeast, Wholegrains, Beansprouts, Bananas, Avocados, Peanuts, Mushrooms
- Currants, Sosmix, Yeast Extract

B1 Thiamin, B2 Riboflavin, B3 Niacin, B6 Pyridoxin, Folic acid, Pantothenic Acid, Biotin, B12 (see next column)

B12*
- Many fortified products: soya milks (Plamil, Unisoy), broccoli, Cabbage, Green Peppers, Parsley, breakfast cereals, Margarine (animal-free), Soya Mince
- Seaweed (esp kelp), Miso, Yeast Extract (fortified eg MERIDIAN)

C
- Green Leafy Vegetables, Broccoli, Cabbage, Green Peppers, Parsley, Potatoes, Frozen Peas, Oranges, Blackcurrants

D
- Sunlight on the skin
- Fortified Cereals (+D2 is animal-free)
- Margarine (animal-free)

E
- Vegetable Oils (esp corn & sunflower)
- Wheatgerm, Tahini, Nuts & Seeds, Avocados

K
- Green Leafy Vegetables, Kelp, Blackstrap Molasses, Vegetables, Oils

MINERALS

IRON (Best absorbed with vitamin C)
- Tofu
- Beans & Pulses (eg Pinto Beans, Baked Beans)
- Green Leafy Vegetables
- Spinach, Cabbage, Wheatgerm, Wholegrains, Parsley, Prunes, Dried Apricots, Pumpkin Seeds, Millet, Blackstrap Molasses (1 tbs = 3.2g)

CALCIUM
- Tofu (4oz = 160mg calcium)
- Tahini (rich source)
- Green Leafy Vegetables, Parsley, Watercress, Broccoli, Swede, Almonds, Brazils, Figs
- Soya Milk (fortified eg Provamel 140mg/100g)

ZINC
- Wholegrains, Wholegrain Rice, Lentils, Pumpkin Seeds, Sesame Seeds, Almonds, Wheatgerm, Oats

IODINE
- Green Leafy Vegetables, Seaweeds, Kelp

NB: Iodine in vegetables depends on soil where grown – Seaweeds are rich source eg NORI, WAKAME, DULSE.

MAGNESIUM
- Green Leafy Vegetables, Soya Beans, Cashew Nuts, Almonds, Broccoli, Wholegrains, Wheatgerm, Bananas, Prunes

PHOSPHOROUS
- Wholegrains, Wholewheat, Pinto Beans, Chick Peas, Pumpkin Seeds, Potatoes, Yeast Extract

SULPHUR / POTASSIUM
- Many Fruits & Vegetables, Nuts

Others: Fluorine/Copper/Cobalt, Chromium/Manganese etc.
- Brewer's Yeast, Green Leafy Vegetables, Bananas, Potatoes, Wholegrains, Almonds, Legumes, Beans & Pulses, Seaweeds

Carbohydrates (COMPLEX - NOT SIMPLE - AVOID SUGAR)
- Wholegrains eg rice, Wholemeal Bread, Potatoes, Beans & Pulses, Cereals, Oats, Pasta

FIBRE – VERY IMPORTANT FOR HEALTH
- Wholegrains, Nuts, Beans & Pulses, Wheatgerm, Oats, Lots of Fruit & Vegetables

eg. Organic. Use what you can.

GENERAL QUESTIONS FOR NUTRITION SOURCES COPYRIGHT 1997
FOR MORE INFORMATION THE VEGAN SOCIETY, 7 BATTLE ROAD, ST LEONARDS-ON-SEA, E. SUSSEX 01424 427393

£12.95

ISBN 0-9536222-0-7
9 780953 622207